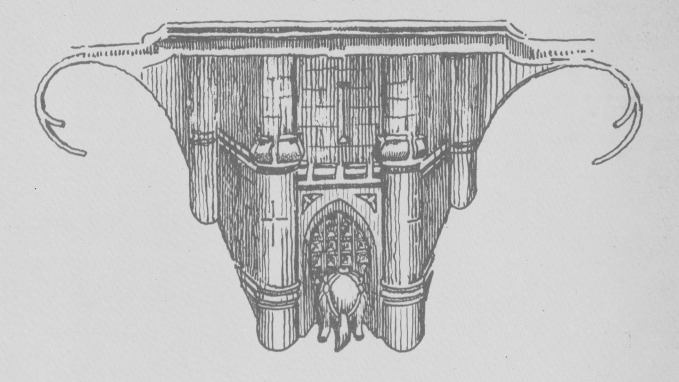

TALES THE HARPER SANG

Medieval Stories collected and retold by
Isabel Wyatt

© The Lanthorn Press 1978
ISBN 0 906155 00 2

MEDIEVAL STORYTELLERS INVOCATION

Before a medieval story-teller began to tell a story, he sang a verse called the Invocation, begging his audience to listen well. Here is an Invocation that he sang before telling an Arthurian story; it is in the English that was spoken in 1400 A.D. There is a free translation of it into modern English on the next page; but before you look at that see how much of this earlier English you can understand:

"Lordingis that are leff and dere,

Lystenyth and I yow telle

By olde dayes what auntures were

Amonge oure eldris that by-felle:

In Arthur dayes, that noble king,

By-felle auntures ferly fele,

And I shall telle of there endynge

That mykell wiste of wo and wele."

from Invocation to The Stanzaic Morte Arthur
1400 A.D.

"My dear lords, pray hearken well,
And I will tales to you unfold
Of wonderous happenings that befell
Our forefathers in days of old:
How they through pain and peril passed
When Arthur ruled (that noble king),
And how to joy they came at last –
Of such adventures shall I sing!"

CONTENTS

THE WELSH BARDS AND THEIR ANCIENT CELTICS STORIES

THE WELSH BARDS AND THEIR ANCIENT CELTIC STORIES

AFTER THE conquest of England by the Anglo-Saxons in the fifth and sixth centuries, the last strongholds of Celtic culture left in Britain were Wales and Cornwall. So it was in these two still unconquered regions that one stream of fugitive Britons found refuge; and it was here that the stories of King Arthur, the great British hero-king, were preserved and carried by wandering minstrels from hall to hall for several hundred years before they were written down.

The Welsh minstrels were called *bards*. They travelled about Wales in companies of twelve. A famous bard named Gwydion, who was known as "the best teller of tales in the whole world", tells us:

"It is a custom with us that the first night after such a company comes to a great man, the chief bard of that band shall have the say. He is invited to tell a tale, and he replies: 'A tale I will tell gladly.' And then he tunes his harp and tells a tale."

We can imagine the scene in the great hall when the evening meal was over and the long trestle table had been taken away – the lord and his family and his guests and his servants all gathered, together with the twelve bards, round the blazing tree-trunk fire, with the boar-hounds and wolf-hounds sleeping on the freshly strewn rushes at their feet. The chief bard tunes his harp; all faces are turned eagerly towards him; and in the gusty torchlight he tells his stirring story, the narrative in chanted prose, the dialogue in verse.

In this way the bards kept the memory of King Arthur green from generation to generation in Wales.

If the lord of the castle was pleased with the harper's minstrelsy in the banqueting-hall, he would often invite him to play and sing to him alone in his bedchamber that night, as, in the Bible, David played his harp to King Saul. The frontispiece is from an illumination painted in the thirteenth century, showing King Mark of Cornwall being played and sung to in this way in his castle at Tintagel. The story tells us that in his hall King Mark said to the minstrel:

"Your playing pleases me so much that you shall sit in my chamber tonight and soothe me with your harping while I lie awake."

Behind the illumination is the music of a thirteenth century song such as this very minstrel might often have played and sung. You can see from it how much change there has been in musical notation since those days.

Our first two stories in this book – *Peredur* and *The Lady of the Fountain* – are two of the ancient Arthurian tales the Welsh bards sang.

Many of the incidents in the Welsh story, *Peredur,* are the same as in the German story, *Parzival,* for these are two names for the same hero. But in *Peredur* the whole background is more primitive, and some of Peredur's wanderings take him to parts of Wales which are still heathen.

Peredur and *The Lady of the Fountain* were first written down in the fourteenth century, in the first collection ever made of the ancient Welsh stories, *The White Book of Rhydderch*. Printing had not yet been invented, so they were written by hand, with quill pens made from feathers, and ink made from oak-galls, on vellum made from sheepskins. All the stories you will be reading in this book were first written in this way.

It was another five hundred years before *Peredur* and *The Lady of the Fountain* were translated out of Welsh into English. This was in the middle of the nineteenth century, when a scholarly mother, Lady Charlotte Guest, turned eleven of the ancient Welsh stories into English for her children. The versions of *Peredur* and *The Lady of the Fountain* you are now going to read are re-told from hers.

You will realize, when you have read them both, that *Peredur* is an older story than *The Lady of the Fountain. Peredur* is certainly more than a thousand years old!

PEREDUR

PEREDUR

I. HOW PEREDUR SET OUT FOR KING ARTHUR'S COURT

PEREDUR was the seventh son of a valiant Welsh Earl. While Peredur was still a babe in arms, his father and his six brothers were all slain in battle. His mother's one wish now was to save her one remaining son from the same fate. So she decided to leave her castle and to take him to live in the wildwood, where he would grow up knowing nothing of chivalry and wars.

As her household, she took with her only women and boys. She forbade them ever to speak to Peredur of the life of castles to which he had been born, or of the customs and ways of the outside world. So he grew from baby to boy, and from boy to youth, knowing nothing of these things.

Then, one day, three knights came riding through the wildwood. They were all three knights of King Arthur; their names were Sir Owain, Sir Gawain and Sir Genir. They were in pursuit of a false knight who had done much harm at King Arthur's Court.

Peredur's mother felt her heart sink when she saw the shining armour of the three knights flashing between the trees.

"What are they, Mother?" Peredur asked.

"They are angels, my son," she told him.

"Then I will go and be an angel, too!" cried Peredur.

And he ran to meet them.

The three knights reined in their steeds. Sir Owain called to him:

"Tell us, good youth, has a knight passed this way?"

"What is a knight?" asked Peredur.

"We three are knights," Sir Owain told him.

"I will answer your questions when you have answered mine," said Peredur.

He asked about their saddles, and their armour, and what knights did; and the three knights told him all he asked.

"How can *I* become a knight?" he ended.

"For that you must go to King Arthur's Court," they told him.

Then he told them that, not long before, he had heard a horse galloping along the track they were on. They thanked him and rode forward; and Peredur ran back to his mother.

"Mother," he said, "those were not angels. They were knights. I am going to King Arthur's Court to be one too."

When she heard this, Peredur's mother fainted. While her women were reviving her, Peredur ran to the stable. From among the pack-horses which brought their food and wine, he chose a bony one which looked to him the strongest. Out of a pack he made a saddle, and wove willows into trappings. He wrapped strips of bark about his legs, and made himself a coat-of-mail out of sackcloth.

In place of a lance he took a pointed ox-goad.

When he came again to his mother, she had revived.

"My son," she said sadly, "will you really leave me?"

"With your leave, Mother," Peredur replied.

"Then do not forget," she told him, "whenever you come to a church, to say your Paternoster before it. If you need meat and drink, take it. If you see a jewel, take it and give it to another. If you meet a fair lady, salute her courteously. If you hear an outcry, seek it out."

"I will remember, Mother," said Peredur.

Then he said farewell to her and to all her household, and rode forth to seek King Arthur's Court.

He had ridden a long way through the forest when he came to a green glade. In it there stood a silken tent so splendid that he said to himself:

"This must be a church. My mother told me always to stop before a church and say my Paternoster."

So he dismounted and stood and said his Paternoster before the doorway of the tent. But when he looked inside, he saw a beautiful maiden sitting in a golden chair. There was a golden ring on her finger; and on a table beside her were loaves of bread and collops of venison and a flask of wine.

"My mother told me," he said to the maiden, "that when I saw meat and drink I was to take them."

"Do so, good youth," said the maiden.

So Peredur ate half of the food and drank half of the wine. Then he knelt on one knee before the maiden, and lifted the hand that wore the golden ring.

"My mother told me," he said, "that when I saw a jewel I was to take it and give it to another."

"Do so, good youth," said the maiden.

So Peredur took the ring and set it on his own finger.

"My mother told me," he said, "that when I met a fair lady I was to salute her courteously."

"Do so, good youth," said the maiden.

So Peredur set a kiss on her cheek. Then he bade her farewell, and mounted his bony horse, and rode on.

Hardly had he gone when the Lord of the Glade returned to the tent.

He saw the hoof marks of Peredur's horse. He saw that half the food had been eaten and that half the wine had been drunk. He asked the maiden:

"Who has been here?"

"A good, simple youth," she told him, "riding a bony pack-horse, wearing a tunic of sackcloth, with an ox-goad for a lance."

"Did he harm you?" he asked.

"He did not," she replied.

"You lie!" said the Lord of the Glade. "Till I find him and take my revenge, you shall not rest two nights in the same house."

And he took the maiden behind him on his steed, and set out to follow Peredur.

II.   HOW PEREDUR CAME TO KING ARTHUR'S COURT

A S Peredur drew near to King Arthur's Court, an unknown knight rode into the hall where the King and all his household sat at meat.

A page was offering to Queen Guinevere a golden goblet brimmed with wine. The stranger snatched it from him, and dashed the wine in the Queen's face.

"If any knight would fight for this goblet," he cried, "and to avenge this insult to the Queen, let him follow me to the Tilting Meadow."

And he turned his horse and rode out of the hall, holding the goblet high.

While all who were sitting at table still gazed at each other in wonder, into the hall rode Peredur.

Sir Kay of the Wry Tongue was standing near the door.

"Tall man," Peredur greeted him, "tell me which is King Arthur."

Sir Kay looked with scorn at the bony horse, the willow trappings, the armour of bark and sackcloth, the ox-goad lance.

"Why do you ask?" he asked sharply.

"My mother gave me leave," said Peredur, "to come to him to be knighted."

At this a dwarf came forward. A whole year he had been at King Arthur's Court, and in all that time not one word had he spoken. But now he called out in greeting:

"Welcome, Peredur, flower of knights!"

"What?" stormed Sir Kay. "You are dumb for a whole year in the midst of King Arthur's knights, then greet this mad fool as the flower of knights?"

And he gave the dwarf such a box on the ear that it felled him to the ground.

Then a female dwarf, the first dwarf's wife, came forward. A whole year she, too, had been at King Arthur's Court, and in all that time not one word had *she* spoken. But now she, too, called out in greeting:

"Welcome, Peredur, flower of knights!"

"What?" stormed Sir Kay, "you, also?"

And he boxed her ears so roughly that she fell beside her husband.

"Tall man," repeated Peredur, "show me which is King Arthur, that he may make me a knight."

"Go to the Tilting Meadow," Sir Kay mocked him, "and overthrow the knight you will find there, and take his horse and armour, and bring back the Queen's goblet. Time enough then to talk of being knighted."

"I will do that, tall man," said Peredur.

And he turned his bony horse and rode out of the hall to where he saw a knight riding proudly up and down the Tilting Meadow with a golden goblet in his hand.

The knight called out to Peredur:

"Did you see anyone coming from the Court?"

"Only myself," said Peredur. "The tall man sent me to overthrow you, and take your horse and armour, and take the Queen's goblet back."

"Fool!" cried the knight. "Go back and tell Arthur to come himself to fight me!"

And he rode towards Peredur in anger, striking him hard on the shoulder with the shaft of his lance.

"When my mother's servants played with me like *that*," said Peredur, "*I* played with them like *this*!"

He lifted his ox-goad to return the blow. But the point ran into the knight's eye, and he fell lifeless to the ground.

Now when Sir Owain heard Sir Kay's sharp words to Peredur, he rose from the table and went to Sir Kay at the door.

"You do wrong," he said, "to send so simple a youth to fight that knight. How can such a knight help but slay him?"

"Go you then and stop him," snarled Sir Kay.

"That I will do," said Sir Owain.

He armed as quickly as he could, and rode swiftly out to the Tilting Meadow. To his relief, Peredur was not dead. He was very much alive, and was dragging the fallen knight to and fro across the meadow.

"Is he dead?" asked Sir Owain.

"He is dead," said Peredur.

"Who slew him?" asked Sir Owain.

"I slew him," said Peredur.

"What are you doing with him now?" asked Sir Owain.

"Getting his iron coat off him," said Peredur.

"I can show you an easier way," said Sir Owain.

And he showed Peredur how to strip off the armour.

"Now you shall put it on," he said, "and mount his steed, and come back with me to King Arthur to be knighted."

"I will put on the armour, and I will mount the steed," said Peredur, "but go back with you I will not."

"And what of the Queen's goblet?" asked Sir Owain.

"You shall take it back to her from me," said Peredur, "and tell her I have avenged the knight's insult."

16 "And what shall I tell King Arthur?" asked Sir Owain.

"Tell him that I count myself his vassal," said Peredur. "But tell him also that I will not come back till I have overthrown the tall man on behalf of the two dwarfs."

Then Sir Owain showed Peredur how to put on the armour, and helped him to mount the knight's steed. He set the knight's lance in his hand, and watched him ride away. Then he stabled Peredur's bony old horse and returned to the hall. And there he gave back the goblet to the Queen and told all these things to King Arthur.

III.   HOW PEREDUR CAME TO THE CASTLES OF HIS UNCLES

EREDUR rode on till he saw a knight riding towards him.

"Whence do you come?" called the knight.

"From King Arthur's Court," said Peredur.

"Are you one of his men?" asked the knight.

"I am," said Peredur.

"That is a pity," said the knight.

"Why so?" asked Peredur.

"Because he is my enemy," said the knight. "And every man I meet of his I slay."

He rode at Peredur furiously. But Peredur handled his lance better than his oxgoad, and overthrew the knight without bloodshed.

"I crave your mercy," cried the knight, prone on the grass.

"Mercy you shall have," said Peredur, "on one condition."

"What is that condition?" asked the knight.

"That you go to King Arthur," said Peredur, "and tell him that I overthrew you in his service, but that I will not return to his Court till I have avenged the dwarfs on the tall man."

"This I pledge my faith to do," said the knight.

And this indeed he did.

During the next seven days Peredur overthrew sixteen more knights, and sent them all to King Arthur with the same message, so that King Arthur said to Sir Kay:

"Alas, Kay, that your wry tongue should have driven such a noble youth away from our Court!"

Still Peredur rode on, till he came to a lake. On the far side was a castle, and near it a kingly old man with white hair was fishing from a boat. When he saw Peredur come riding along the lake-shore, he rose and went into the castle.

When Peredur reached the castle and was brought into its hall, the kingly old man was sitting on a cushion before a blazing fire; and when Peredur had unarmed and been given fresh garments, he sat there beside him till they went to meat.

After they had eaten, the kingly old man asked him:

"Do you know well how to fight with a sword?"

"I have never tried," said Peredur. "If I were taught, I think I would."

"Those who can play well with cudgel and shield," said the old man, "can also fight well with a sword."

He called his two sons to him and bade them play with cudgel and shield. He bade

Peredur watch them well.

Presently he asked:

"Which do you think is the better?"

"The one with the yellow hair," said Peredur.

"Take the other's cudgel and shield, and see if you can do better than the better one," said the old man.

Peredur did as he was bidden. Presently he gave the yellow-haired youth such a blow that the blood flowed down from his brow.

"Come now and sit down," said the old man to Peredur. "I am your uncle, your mother's brother. You will be a mighty fighter with the sword when you have grown to your full strength. But take care never to ask questions without good cause."

Next morning Peredur took leave of his uncle and his two cousins, and again rode on. As evening fell, he came to another castle; when he was brought into the hall, he found there another kingly white-haired old man, as much like the first one as one pea is like another, except that this one was lame.

After they had eaten, this one also asked Peredur:

"Do you know well how to fight with a sword?"

Peredur gave the same reply:

"I have never tried. If I were taught, I think I would."

There was a great iron staple set in the floor of the hall. The old man put a sword in Peredur's hand and bade him strike the staple with it. He did so; and both sword and staple broke in two.

The old man bade him place the broken parts together. When Peredur did so, the broken staple united, and so did the broken sword.

"Now strike again," said the old man.

A second time Peredur struck. A second time both staple and sword were broken. A second time he united them.

A third time Peredur struck. A third time both staple and sword were broken. But this time neither would unite.

"Come now and sit down," said the old man then. "I am your uncle, your mother's second brother. You have come to two thirds of your strength. When you have grown to your full power, you will be the best swordsman in all this Island of Britain."

When Peredur was seated, silence fell on the hall. Two youths bore in a mighty spear; from its tip, streams of blood were flowing. Then two maidens bore in a salver on which lay a man's head. The whole company wept; and Peredur greatly wondered. But he reminded himself:

"My first uncle told me never to ask questions without good cause."

And so he did not ask the meaning of it all.

IV.   HOW PEREDUR RESTORED A MAIDEN'S EARLDOM

**N**EXT morning Peredur took leave of his second uncle, and again rode forward. As he drew near to a wood, he heard a loud outcry within it.

"My mother told me," he said to himself, "if I heard an outcry, to seek it out."

So he rode towards it, and found among the trees a beautiful lady seated on the ground. A man's body lay across her knees, and she was bowed over it, weeping very piteously.

"Lady," said Peredur, drawing rein beside her, "tell me how I can aid you."

She looked up; and as soon as she saw him she cried:

"*You* aid me, Peredur? You, who caused your mother's death when you left her against her wish? I am your foster-sister; and now, alas, my husband has been slain by the knight who roams this forest."

"Sister," said Peredur, "as soon as we have laid him to rest I will seek out this knight who has slain him."

When they had laid the body to rest, Peredur rode forward in quest of the knight. Presently he saw him pricking proudly towards him among the trees.

"Whence do you come?" called the knight.

"From King Arthur's Court," said Peredur.

"Are you one of his men?" asked the knight.

"I am," said Peredur.

"That is a pity," said the knight.

"Why so?" asked Peredur.

"Because he is my enemy," said the knight. "And every man of his I meet, I slay."

They set their lances at rest and charged each other. At the very first encounter, Peredur overthrew the knight.

"I crave your mercy," cried the knight, prone on the ground.

"Mercy you shall have," said Peredur, "on two conditions."

"What are those two conditions?" asked the knight.

"The first," said Peredur, "is that you shall guard with your own life this lady whose lord you have slain, and care for her welfare, and protect her dominions."

"This I pledge my faith to do," said the knight. "And the second condition?"

"That you go to King Arthur," said Peredur, "and tell him that I overthrew you in his service, but that I will not return to his Court till I have avenged the dwarfs on the tall man."

"This also I pledge my faith to do," said the knight.

And both indeed he did.

Every knight with whom Peredur fought he overthrew. And every knight whom he overthrew he sent to King Arthur with the same message. At last Sir Owain said to the king:

"This noble youth will never return to your Court till Kay goes forth from it."

"We must find him," said the King, "so that he and Kay may meet each other in single combat.

So King Arthur and a band of his knights set out in search of Peredur.

Meanwhile Peredur still rode forward till he came to a castle in the midst of bushes and briars. He struck the gate with the shaft of his lance; it was opened by a tall, thin youth with red hair, very sad of face and clad in a ragged surcoat, who welcomed him most courteously and brought him into the hall.

Here Peredur found eighteen other youths and young men, all tall and thin, all with red hair, all very sad of face, and all clad in ragged surcoats. With them was one of the fairest maidens his eyes had ever beheld, but as sad of face as the youths were, and clad in a gown of tattered satin.

All of them welcomed Peredur most courteously.

Presently two nuns came into the hall. One bore a flagon of wine; the other bore six loaves of white bread.

"Alas, Lady," they said to the maiden, "this is all the meat and drink we can bring to you this night. It is all we have in our convent."

The maiden thanked the nuns; and they all sat down to eat. The bread and wine they shared among them. The table was bare of all other meats.

That night, when Peredur was asleep in his chamber, he awoke to the sound of his door being softly opened. A lighted candle appeared, and the maiden entered. She was sobbing quietly but as if her heart would break.

"Lady, what ails you?" asked Peredur.

"I will tell you, Lord," she said. "I was my father's only child, and at his death he left me his earldom. The Earl whose lands lie next to mine has snatched mine from me piece by piece till I have only this castle left. And at break of day he is coming with all his men to take this also, and to bear me away a captive and to give me to his grooms."

"What forces have you to man the castle?" Peredur asked her.

"Of all my household," she told him, "only my nineteen foster-brothers are left alive."

"What food have you in the castle in case of siege?" he asked her next.

"None," she told him. "The nuns have fed us till they also have nothing left."

"Go now and sleep, Lady," said Peredur. "And weep no more. Tomorrow I will meet this Earl."

She went thankfully to her chamber. And Peredur slept again.

At break of day he awoke to the sound of trumpets blowing and horses neighing. He arose and looked down from his window. The ground outside the castle gate was covered with tents and thronged with knights as at the siege of some great city.

Quickly Peredur armed and called for his horse. Then alone he rode through the castle gate; alone he confronted that great army.

A knight rode proudly towards him and challenged him to single combat. At once they charged each other. They broke a set of lances; then Peredur called up his full strength and suddenly overthrew him.

"I crave your mercy," cried the knight. "I will not conceal from you that I am Master of the Household to the Earl."

"Mercy you shall have," said Peredur, "if you yield yourself with all your men to the Countess of this castle, and go at once to her with them, taking with you store of food.

"This I pledge my faith to do," said the knight.

And at once he did so.

Then a second knight rode proudly towards Peredur, on a steed prancing and strong and spirited. He challenged him to single combat; and at once they charged each other.

They broke a set of lances; they broke a second set. Then Peredur called up his full strength, and suddenly overthrew him.

"I crave your mercy," cried the knight. "I will not conceal from you that I am Steward of the Palace to the Earl."

"Mercy you shall have," said Peredur, "if you yield yourself with all your men to the Countess of this castle, and go at once to her with them, taking with you store of food."

"This I pledge my faith to do," said the knight.

And at once he did so.

Then a third knight rode towards Peredur, on a war-horse high-mettled and proudly snorting. He challenged him to single combat; and at once they charged each other.

They broke a set of lances; they broke a second set; they broke a third. Then Peredur called up his full strength, and suddenly overthrew him.

"I crave your mercy," cried the knight. " I will not conceal from you that I am the Earl himself."

"Mercy you shall have," said Peredur, "if you restore to the Countess her earldom, and yield yourself with all your men to her."

"This I pledge my faith to do," said the knight.

And at once he did so.

Peredur stayed only long enough to see all in the castle set once more in order. Then he took leave of the Countess and her nineteen foster-brothers, and again he rode forward.

V.   HOW PEREDUR MET A SORCERESS, AND HOW HE FELL TO MUSING IN THE SNOW

WHEN Peredur had ridden for some days, he entered a forest; and in it he met a lady riding on a lean old palfrey. Her face was sorrowful; her garments were stained with long travel.

Peredur saluted her with courtesy, and asked her wither she was bound.

"My lord and I are wandering," she replied, "in search of a good, simple youth. My lord will not permit me to rest two nights in any house until he finds and fights this youth. For he says, though it is not true, that I have been unfaithful to him with this youth."

Peredur looked again at her; and under the rags and the sadness he thought he could see the beautiful maiden whose tent he had taken for a church when first he had left his mother. As he looked again to make sure, the Lord of the Glade came riding at a gallop towards them.

"Have you met a youth anywhere in this forest," he called to Peredur, "riding a bony pack-horse, wearing a tunic of sackcloth, and with an ox-goad for a lance?"

"I am that youth," said Peredur.

The Lord of the Glade rode at him as if he would ride him down. They splintered their lances; then their swords struck sparks of fire from each other's armour. Then Peredur called up his full strength, and the Lord of the Glade lay prone at his feet.

"I crave your mercy," he cried.

"Mercy you shall have," said Peredur, "on this condition: that you return by the way you came, and everywhere proclaim that this lady is innocent."

"This I pledge my faith to do," said the Lord of the Glade.

And this he did.

When Peredur parted from them, he rode on through the forest till he came to a land laid waste, as if by war. Towards nightfall he came to a castle. A youth led him into its hall, where a stately lady greeted him. When they had eaten together, she said to him:

"Sir, you would find it safer to go elsewhere to sleep."

"Why so, Lady?" asked Peredur.

"The Nine Sorceresses of Gloucester have laid my whole land waste," she told him. "Tomorrow one of them will storm this castle and slay my son and myself. Unless you leave us before daybreak, you will share our fate."

"With your leave, Lady," said Peredur, "I will await her with you."

So Peredur slept that night in the castle.

At daybreak he was awakened by a dreadful outcry. He rose and looked out, and saw the castle guards fleeing all ways at once. Standing sword in hand on the ramparts was a terrible hag with flaming eyes and with wild hair streaming from beneath her helmet.

Peredur snatched up his sword. Running down the corkscrew stairs and leaping on to the ramparts, he struck the hag such a blow that her helmet lay as flat as a dish on her head.

"I crave your mercy, Peredur," she shrieked.

"How do you know I am Peredur?" he asked.

"Because this blow was foretold," she said. "Also it was foretold that I should teach you the ways and customs of war and of the world you were not taught in the wildwood."

"Mercy you shall have," said Peredur, "on one condition: that you give back her lands to the lady of this castle, and that never again do you or your sisters do harm to her or to them."

"This I pledge my faith to do," she said.

And this she did.

When Peredur had seen all fulfilled to his liking, he took his leave of the lady of the castle, and went with the Sorceress to the palace in which she lived with her sisters. And there he was well taught in those ways and customs of war and of the world that his mother had kept from him in the wildwood.

When his training was ended, he once more went on his way.

It led him to a valley in which snow had fallen. On the snow lay a dead bird, and near it stood the raven that had just killed it. Peredur reined in his horse, staring at the blackness of the raven and the redness of the dead bird's blood against the whiteness of the snow.

He thought of the maiden whose earldom he had restored. Her hair was as black as the raven; her lips were as red as the blood; her skin was as white as the snow.

He sat on his horse as still as if he had been turned to stone, so deep in his musing that he was lost to all outward things.

VI. HOW PEREDUR CAME AGAIN TO KING ARTHUR'S COURT

ING Arthur's search for Peredur had brought him to that same valley; and now he said to Sir Genir:

"Who is that knight who stands so still up yonder?"

"Sire," said Sir Genir, "I do not know, but I will go and ask."

So Sir Genir rode up the valley to Peredur and asked him who he was; but Peredur was sunk so deep in his musing that he did not reply. Then Sir Genir thrust his lance at Peredur to wake him up; and Peredur turned and unhorsed him with one stroke, then went back to his musing.

When Sir Genir rode back to King Arthur's camp with this story, four and twenty other knights went to Peredur, one by one. To not one did he reply, but unhorsed each in turn with a single thrust, then turned back to his musing.

At last Sir Kay of the Wry Tongue said:

"It rests with me, it seems, to teach this puppy manners."

And he rode angrily up the valley towards Peredur.

When he came near to him, he called to him rudely, and Peredur turned and unhorsed him with one thrust, then went back to his musing.

Sir Kay had fallen so heavily that he had broken both his arm and his shoulder; so there he lay in the snow, unable to move. Great was everyone's surprise when his horse came back to the camp without a rider, for Sir Kay was the best horseman at King Arthur's Court. A band of the knights rode at once up the valley, taking a horse-litter with them; and in this they brought Sir Kay back to the camp, where King Arthur had him placed in the royal tent, and had his own chief physician, Morgant the Wise, brought to attend him there.

All the time the band of knights had moved round Peredur, it had been to him as if he sat his horse alone in the snow-filled valley. So now Sir Gawain said to King Arthur:

"Sire, if it seems well to you, I myself will ride out to this knight."

From King Arthur's bed Sir Kay broke in spitefully:

"He is weary now with fighting. It will be easy for you to take him now the rest of us have paved the way."

"It was not in my mind to take him," said Sir Gawain, "but to invite him courteously to visit the King at his camp."

For so famed was Sir Gawain for his courteous speech that he was called the

Golden-Tongued.

"With your soft tongue," spat Sir Kay, "a coat of thin linen is armour enough for you. You will not need to break either lance or sword to bring him in."

"I hope," said Sir Gawain, "not to need to break arm or shoulder, either."

"Go, Gawain," said King Arthur hastily.

And Sir Gawain went.

He found Peredur resting on the shaft of his spear, still musing. He drew rein beside him and saluted him courteously; then he said:

"Sir, if I thought it would be as agreeable to you as it would be to me, I would talk with you; for King Arthur prays you to come and visit him at his camp yonder."

"Ah, is that why those other knights came?" asked Peredur. "They broke in rudely upon my thoughts of a lady with hair as black as that raven, and lips as red as that blood, and skin as white as this snow."

"I do not marvel," said Sir Gawain, "that you found it displeasing to be disturbed in such gentle thoughts."

"Tell me," said Peredur, "is Sir Kay with King Arthur?"

"He is," replied Sir Gawain. "You broke his arm and shoulder with your absent-minded thrust."

"Ah," said Peredur, "then I have avenged the dwarfs and am free to return to King Arthur's Court."

Sir Gawain, wondering, looked closely at Peredur and begged to be told his name. "I am called Peredur," said Peredur. "And who are you?"

"I am called Gawain," said Gawain.

"That is a name I have heard well spoken of," said Peredur. "I would be glad to have your friendship."

"Gladly do I give it," said Gawain. "And I beg you to grant me yours."

"I do so as gladly," said Peredur.

So they rode joyfully together to the camp. Through the doorway of King Arthur's tent Sir Kay saw them coming.

"I knew Gawain would not need to fight," he said bitterly. "He can do more with his fair words than I with my strong arm."

In Gawain's tent he and Peredur took off their armour and arrayed themselves in fresh garments. Then Gawain brought Peredur to King Arthur.

"See, Sire," he said, "here is that goodly Peredur whom you have sought so long."

"Welcome, Peredur," said King Arthur. "Too long have we waited to knight you."

Then King Arthur knighted Peredur, and took him back with him to his Court, rejoicing greatly. And there Sir Peredur was received graciously by Queen Guinevere and her ladies, and all King Arthur's good knights welcomed him into their fellowship.

Now among Queen Guinevere's ladies was one called Angarad of the Golden Hand. Day after day Sir Peredur looked at her; and always it seemed to him that she was the loveliest lady his eyes had ever beheld.

At last one day he said to her:

"Lady, if it were pleasing to you, I could love you above all women."

"It is not pleasing," said Angarad. "For never could I love *you*."

"I pledge my faith," said Peredur, "that until you come to love me above all other men, I will not speak another word to any Christian."

He went to his lodging, and secretly prepared to leave the Court. Without any leave-takings, he departed next morning at daybreak. Those parts of the Island of Britain which were Christian he left behind him, and made his way towards those parts which were still pagan.

VII. HOW PEREDUR CAME TO THE VALLEY OF THE PAGANS

RIDING one day along a mountain ridge, Peredur saw below him a round valley. Its sides were scattered with dwellings, huge and black and rudely built. But nowhere could he see church or chapel or abbey or hermitage or cross or wayside shrine. So he knew that he had indeed come into the country of the pagans.

A rocky ledge wound downwards round the valley. Peredur dismounted, and led his horse carefully along it.

Near the valley bottom he came upon a lion stretched across this narrow track. He was chained and sleeping, and there was no way forward except the way he guarded. A deep chasm yawned beneath him, half filled with bones, both of horses and of men.

Peredur drew his sword and smote the lion, so that it fell into the pit and hung there by its chain. Then Peredur smote the chain, so that it snapped, and the lion fell upon the bones piled far below. Mounting his horse, Peredur spurred him on to leap across the chasm; they landed safely on the other side, and went on towards a great grey palace at the valley's foot.

In the meadow before the palace an old grey man was sitting, larger than any human being Peredur had ever seen. Two young men were sitting beside him, one with yellow hair and one with red.

They rose and came to meet Peredur.

"Are you pagan or Christian?" asked the one with yellow hair.

With his finger Peredur drew a cross upon the air.

"Do not do that in this valley!" cried the young man with red hair. "Do you not know that you have come to the Valley of the Pagans?"

"I dared not speak till I knew," said Peredur, "for I am pledged to speak to no Christian till the lady I love loves *me*."

The young men laughed.

"Take no care for that," said one.

And the other added:

"For you will never speak again to *any* Christian."

They led him to the grey old man, who muttered:

"Disgrace to the beard of my porter!"

"Do not miscall your lion," the young men laughed. "For this stranger is a Christian, who will give your vassals good sport."

Then they went all four together into that primitive palace, and sat down to meat

25

with a stately old woman and with a young one as stately. This maiden and Peredur were seated side by side.

"Sir, are you a Christian?" she asked.

"I am," said Peredur.

"Alas," she whispered, "for then you are doomed."

"How so?" asked Peredur.

"In the great black houses in this valley," she told him, "live pagan giants who are my father's vassals. At daybreak they will come and slay you. Never yet has any Christian who has come into our valley gone out of it alive."

Peredur thought awhile. Then he asked:

"Maiden, can you cause my horse and armour to be lodged with me tonight?"

"Sir, I both can and will," she said.

And this she did.

Before daybreak Peredur rose and donned his armour. He led his horse round the pagan palace till he found a recess in the wall where only one at a time could attack him. Here he mounted his horse and waited.

At daybreak he heard a great tumult as the giants came crowding into the meadow, all agog for their sport. When they saw where Peredur had chosen to meet them, a great outcry arose. Then the stately old woman came to the grey old man and pleaded:

"Husband, let this stranger go, for I fear his life will cost many.'"

"That may not be," he replied. "If any Christian goes forth alive, all in the valley must be baptised."

So the giants came to attack Peredur one by one; and one by one he slew them.

Then the maiden came to the grey old man and pleaded:

"Father, your vassals are dying like flies. Let this stranger go."

"That may not be," he said a second time.

Then the young man with yellow hair attacked Peredur and was slain.

"Husband," said the stately old woman, "now we have only one son left. Let the stranger go."

"That may not be," he said a third time.

Then the young man with the red hair attacked Peredur and was also slain.

"Father," said the maiden, "now *you* have no son and *I* no brother left."

The grey old man sighed deeply and hid his face in his hands. After a while he lifted it and said to her:

"Go to the stranger and crave mercy for us all. We will yield ourselves into his hands."

The maiden came to Peredur, and brought him her father's message. Peredur sent back by her this message to the grey old man:

"Mercy you shall have, on two conditions. One is that you shall go to King Arthur and pay him homage. And the other is that you, with all who dwell in this valley, shall be baptised."

"All this will we do," said the grey old man.

That night Peredur slept again in the pagan palace. Next morning the grey old man set out for King Arthur's Court, and Peredur also came forth out of the valley. Along the mountain ridge he rode forward till he came to a desert in which he could still keep his vow not to speak to any Christian, for there he could speak to nobody at all.

VIII. HOW PEREDUR WON ANGARAD'S LOVE AND HOW HE HEARD OF THE MOUND OF MOURNING

PEREDUR dwelt alone in the desert till his armour was rusty and the colours had faded from his shield; till his skin was burnt black by its suns; till both he and his steed were as gaunt as his first bony packhorse. He dewlt there alone until, from long lack of speaking, the need to speak went from him. Then he set out again for King Arthur's Court.

As he drew near to it, he met Sir Kay and Sir Gawain riding out in King Arthur's service. To them he looked a stranger, and a stranger stranger than they had ever seen. Sir Kay called to him rudely, demanding his name; Peredur remained silent. Sir Kay called a second time; still Peredur remained silent. At last Sir Kay, angered, thrust at him with his lance, wounding him in the thigh.

Peredur gave no counter-thrust, but rode on, still silent.

"Kay," said Gawain, "that was ill-done."

And he turned back, and overtook Peredur, and rode with him to the Court; and there he brought him to Queen Guinevere.

"Lady," he said, "since I must away on the King's service, I commit this dumb stranger to your care."

The Queen sent at once for Morgant the Wise, King Arthur's chief physician, and gave Peredur into the care of her ladies until his wound should be healed. Among these ladies was Angarad of the Golden Hand. She was filled with pity for the dumb stranger; and he was filled with joy for her gentleness and kindness. By the time his wound was healed, he had won her heart.

But still be kept his vow and never spoke; and so he became known to all the Court as the Dumb Youth.

One day, when King Arthur and his household were on their way to church, they saw a knight riding to and fro in the Tilting Meadow, with his pennon raised in the challenge to combat. King Arthur sent attendants to fetch his own horse and arms, that he might tilt with him; but on their way back, Peredur took both horse and arms from them, and himself came pricking into the meadow to do battle with the knight.

All the Court came flocking to look on. They saw the two knights thunder to the attack; they saw the Dumb Youth stand firm under the encounter, then spur his horse and thrust so strongly with his lance that he lifted the knight sheer out of his saddle and cast him clean away.

While attendants gave aid to the overthrown knight, Peredur gave back King Arthur's horse and arms, and returned on foot to the palace. Angarad came to meet him.

"Ah, Dumb Youth," she cried, "if only you could speak, I would love you above all men. And even though you cannot, I still love you best of all."

"So love I you," said Peredur.

The news spread through the Court that the Dumb Youth had spoken, and that who should he be but goodly Peredur! Great was the wonder, and great the rejoicing. So Peredur remained at Court in great content.

Then one day he went hunting with King Arthur.

Peredur's hound started a hart; the hound followed the hart, and Peredur followed the hound. The hart went into a forest, and through the forest, and out of the forest; and still the hound followed the hart, and still Peredur followed the hound. When at last the hound overtook the hart, and killed it, Peredur for the first time looked about him. He saw that he was lost on an unknown barren heath.

Evening was already falling, and he looked about him for some shelter for the night. Far away on the edge of the heath he saw a light, and towards this he rode.

The light was streaming through the open doorway of a hall. He dismounted and went in. In the hall were three maidens, sitting on a bench; he saluted them courteously, and went and sat beside them. At once all three maidens began to weep. "Maidens, why do you weep?" asked Peredur.

"Because tonight you will be slain," said the first maiden.

"Who will slay me?" asked Peredur.

"Our father," said the second maiden.

"Why will he slay me?" asked Peredur.

"Because he slays everyone who comes hither without his leave," said the third maiden.

Even as she spoke, they heard a tumult outside. Then a man entered the hall; he was huge and black, and he had only one eye.

The maidens rose, and helped him to take off his armour, and brought him fresh garments. Then he sat down, and turned to Peredur, and asked:
"What brought you hither?"

"Chance," the first maiden told him.

"He did not come to spy," the second maiden added.

"So grant him his life," the third maiden pleaded.

"I will grant it for this one night," said the one-eyed man.

Then they all ate and drank together. The wine was the strongest Peredur had ever tasted; without his will he found himself asking:
"Black man, how did you lose your other eye?"

"For that question," cried the black man, "you certainly shall die."

"But not till tomorrow," begged the three maidens.

And the black man agreed.

At daybreak he came to Peredur's chamber.
"Arise and die," he said.

But Peredur had already arisen and was awaiting him in his armour, his sword in his hand. They fought. It was not long before the black man was craving mercy.

"Mercy you shall have," said Peredur, "on two conditions. The first is that you shall slay no more knights who enter your hall in peace."

"To this I pledge my faith," the black man said. "And the second?"

"The second", said Peredur, "is that you tell me how you lost your eye."

"Hear, then," said the black man. "Two days' march away there is a mound called the Mound of Mourning. On the mound there is a cairn. In the cairn there is a serpent. On the tail of the serpent there is a stone. Whoever holds that stone in one hand will hold in the other all the gold he desires. It was in fighting this serpent that I lost my eye."

And the moment Peredur heard of the Mound of Mourning, he wanted nothing so much as to set out in search of it.

IX.   HOW PEREDUR SLEW THE ADDANC

PEREDUR set out at once on his way to the Mound of Mourning. At sunset he came to a palace. The door of its hall stood wide open; and from it there came to meet him three princesses in golden crowns.

They brought him into the hall, and unarmed him, and clothed him in fresh garments. They did all this with great courtesy; yet all the time the door was left wide open and they kept turning towards it as if listening and waiting.

As dusk fell, Peredur heard the thud of hoof-beats coming nearer; then a charger galloped through the open door into the hall. On its back was a golden saddle; and in the saddle sat a dead prince, with a golden crown over his helmet.

The three princesses lifted him from the saddle. They anointed him with balsam from a silver flagon. He rose up alive, and came to Peredur, and greeted him with joy.

Then a second charger bore a second dead prince into the hall. The three princesses anointed him in the same way. He also rose up alive. Then came a third charger, bearing a third dead prince; he, too, was restored to life.

Then the hall was filled with joy; and Peredur sat down to eat with the three princes and the three princesses.

"If it would be agreeable to *you*", said Peredur, "it would be agreeable to *me* to hear the meaning of what I have seen."

"Hear, then," said the first prince. "In a cave beyond the mountain lurks an Addanc. He can see all men; but no man can see *him*. There is a standing-stone in the doorway of the cave; and from behind this he slays with his glance all who come near."

"Every sunrise," said the second prince, "we three brothers ride to the cave. Every noon the Addanc slays us with his glance. Every dusk our chargers bear our bodies home; and our sisters anoint us and bring us back to life."

"Must this go on for ever?" Peredur asked.

"It must go on," the third prince told him, "till someone slays the Addanc. Then we shall be free from this spell."

Then Peredur begged them to permit him to go with them next morning.

But the eldest princess asked:

"Have you the stone that renders a man invisible?"

And when he said he had not, the middle princess said:

"Then you must not go; for the Addanc would slay you, too."

And the youngest princess added:

"And we have power to bring only our brothers back to life."

But Peredur rose before sunrise, and put on his armour and muffled his horse's hoofs. And when the princes bade their sisters farewell and rode away, he rode silently after them.

Presently they passed out of sight round the side of a mountain. When Peredur in turn came round the mountain, he saw a mound beside the track; and on the mound sat a lady. She was as dainty as if made of flowers.

"Stay, Peredur," she said. "You are chosen to slay the Addanc. The Addanc can now see all men but no man can see him. But if you bear this stone in your hand, *you* will see *him* and *he* will not see *you*."

She laid the stone in his hand. And straightway she turned into a pale mist which thinned away into clear air.

Peredur rode forward, the stone in his hand, till he came to a river. On one side of it was a flock of white sheep, on the other a flock of black sheep. Whenever a white sheep bleated, a black one swam across the river and became white; whenever a black sheep bleated, a white one swam across the river and became black.

Beside the river grew a tall tree. One half was full of green leaves from root to top; the other half was full of flames. Beneath the tree was a mound; and on the mound sat a young king in a golden crown, with two greyhounds lying beside him.

There were three tracks winding away from the mound; two of them were wide and one was narrow. Peredur greeted the young king courteously and asked him where the tracks went.

"The widest track goes to my palace," said the young king. "Stay with me to watch the chase, then return there with me."

"I thank you," replied Peredur, "but I may not tarry, pleasant though that would be."

"The next widest track," the young king went on, "goes to the city, where food may also be found."

"I may not linger even for that," said Peredur.

"The narrowest track," the young king told him, "leads to the cave of the Addanc."

"That is the way I must go," said Peredur.

They exchanged courteous farewells, and Peredur rode forward along the narrow track.

It was already noon when he reached the cave. Outside it he saw three chargers standing, and on each charger a golden saddle, and in each saddle a dead prince sitting.

Stone in left hand, lance in right hand, Peredur rode past them into the cave.

He saw the fearsome Addanc. He was crouching behind the standing-stone and looking right through Peredur as if he had been clear air. Peredur thrust him through. Then he cut off his monstrous head, and turned his horse and rode out again with the head at his saddle-bow.

The three dead princes began to stir in their golden saddles. When they saw Peredur riding out of the cave with the Addanc's head, they all three cried out in joy;

"We thank you, goodly Peredur."

"How do you know my name?" asked Peredur, astonished.

"It was foretold," they told him, "that one day the goodly Peredur should free us from this spell."

He gave the Addanc's head into their charge, and they begged him to return with them to their palace. But he replied, as he had replied to the young king:

"I thank you, but I may not tarry, pleasant though that would be."

So, after courteous farewells, the three princes rode back to their sisters, and Peredur rode forward towards the Mound of Mourning.

X.   THE MOUND OF MOURNING; AND HOW PEREDUR FARED AT THE TOURNAMENT

PRESENTLY, Peredur heard a thud of hoofs behind him. Looking back, he saw a young man in red armour riding a red horse furiously towards him. He drew rein and waited.

"Lord," said the young man, as he drew alongside, "I have a boon to beg."

"What boon is that?" asked Peredur.

"That you take me as your squire," said the young man.

"Whom then would I be taking as my squire?" asked Peredur.

"I am called Etlym of the Red Sword," the young man told him. "I will not conceal from you that I am an Earl."

"I am but an Earl myself," said Peredur. "Since you wish to be my squire, my squire you shall be."

They rode on together till they came to a great mound. On the mound was a cairn. All round the mound there were pitched three hundred tents; and within the tents, three hundred knights were sitting.

Peredur said to his new squire:

"Go to those knights, and ask them why they are here."

This Etlym did.

"This is the Mound of Mourning," they replied. "We are guarding the serpent in the cairn until he dies."

When Peredur heard this, he, too, rode to them and asked:

"And what will you do then?"

"We will fight among ourselves for the stone on his tail," they told him.

"Wait here instead," said Peredur, "while I fight the serpent."

"No," they said. "Let us all fight the serpent."

"I pledge my faith," said Peredur, "that if I slay the serpent and win the stone, you shall all have all the gold that you desire."

"Go then and fight him, Lord," they said.

Peredur climbed the mound, and the serpent came forth from the cairn. Peredur fought the serpent, and slew it, and took the stone from its tail. Then he came down to the three hundred knights, and he gave to each of them all the gold that each desired. But to Etlym he gave the stone itself, saying:

"My mother told me, when I saw a jewel, to take it and give it to another."

Then Peredur sent Etlym back to the Countess who was Etlym's bride, and he himself rode forward alone till he came to a valley as full of tents as it would hold. All round this valley there were more windmills and water-mills than he had ever seen before.

He saw a tall man in a workman's garment standing near by. He rode up to him and asked him who he was.

"I am the miller," he said, "set over all these mills."

"Why are there so many?" Peredur asked.

"To grind corn for all the knights in all these tents," the miller told him.

"And why are *they* so many?" Peredur asked.

"They have come," said the miller, "to take part in the tournament that is being held in honour of the Empress of Cristinobyl."

Peredur decided that he also would take part in this tournament. He asked the miller if he could give him lodging; the miller said he could, and he took him home with him to his pleasant dwelling. The miller's wife was not pleased when Peredur borrowed money from her husband; but Peredur promised to repay it out of the prizes he would win in the tournament.

Next morning Peredur armed himself, and mounted his horse, and rode towards the meadow in which the tournament was to be held. But on the way he came to the fairest tent that he had ever seen, and, leaning from its window, the fairest maiden. It seemed to him that he had once met her in a dream; and he reined in his horse, and remained gazing at her from morning to noon and from noon to sunset; and by then the tournament was over for that day.

So Peredur returned to his lodging to take off his armour; and the miller's wife asked him what prizes he had won. She was angry when he said he had won none; but he promised to do better the next day. But the next day also he spent gazing at the maiden. And again the miller's wife was angry when he returned at sunset with no prizes.

The third morning, as again he sat gazing at the maiden, he was almost unhorsed by a mighty blow between his shoulders. He turned, and there stood the miller.

"Do one of two things," begged the miller. "Either go to the tournament and win some prizes, or come no more within reach of my wife's tongue."

Then Peredur smiled at the miller; and the miller smiled at Peredur; and Peredur rode forward to the tournament; and every knight he fought he overthrew.

The horse and armour of every knight he overthrew he sent to the miller's wife; for when a knight was overthrown in a tournament, his horse and armour belonged to the knight who overthrew him. So horse and armour followed horse and armour to the miller's wife throughout the day, till the granary was piled high with helmets and coats-of-mail, and the mill was packed with horses standing head to tail.

At sunset the Empress of Cristinobyl sent for Peredur, that he might receive the prize for that day's tilting; and when he was brought to her tent, it was the tent outside which he had stayed gazing; and when he was ushered into the presence of the Empress, he found she was the maiden at whom he had gazed.

As she gave him that day's prize, a golden ring set with a ruby, she smiled at him, and said:

"Peredur, do you not remember me? It was I who gave you the stone on your way to the cave of the Addanc."

"Ah, Lady," said Peredur, "I do indeed remember now."

And they made great cheer together till the tournament was ended.

XI.   THE COMING OF THE BLACK MAIDEN

HEN, loaded with gifts and with honour, Peredur returned to King Arthur's Court; and all who were there were glad at his coming. Angarad welcomed him lovingly, and he had great joy in the fellowship of the knights.

One day, King Arthur was seated in his hall on a golden chair; and at his feet, on a carpet of velvet, sat Peredur, with Sir Owain and Sir Gawain and Sir Howel. Suddenly into the hall came a yellow mule, ridden by a hideous maiden who was blacker than pitch.

She greeted King Arthur by name, and Sir Owain and Sir Gawain and Sir Howel. But Peredur she did not greet. Instead, she cried out to him fiercely:

"Ah, Peredur, whom men call Goodly Peredur, what a different tale could I tell of you! When you saw the bleeding spear at the castle of the Lame King, if only you had asked its meaning, his lameness would have been healed, and his land would be at peace. Instead, many are the kingdoms that are laid waste, and many are the men who must die, and all because of you!"

"Ah!" cried Peredur. "What then *is* the meaning of the bleeding spear?"

"It can only be found in the castle in which I dwell," she said. "And there also whoever deserves fame and honour will learn the way to gain them."

"Maiden, where is this castle?" King Arthur asked.

"Sire," she replied, "the way to it lies through the Castle of Wonders."

And she turned her yellow mule, and smote it with her jagged thong, and so rode out of the hall.

Then Peredur said:

"I shall not rest till I have found the meaning of the bleeding spear."

And Sir Gawain said:

"Nor I till I find if I deserve fame and honour."

So these two went out, each to his own lodging, and each put on his armour, and called for his horse, and said farewell to King Arthur and all his Court.

Because of their great friendship, they set forth together. But when they came to a crossroads, Gawain said:

"Two different ways will bring us each to different adventures."

"Then let us part," said Peredur, "pledging our faith to meet at the black maiden's castle beyond the Castle of Wonders."

So they pledged their faith to do this, and then they parted.

Peredur rode forward. For many months he rode, seeking tidings of the Castle of Wonders. But he could meet with none.

Then, one evening, as he was riding through a valley, he overtook a priest, and asked his blessing.

"You merit no blessing," replied the priest, "and would profit nothing by it, seeing that you ride clad in armour on such a day as this."

"What day then *is* this?" asked Peredur.

"Are you a Christian," cried the priest, "and do not know it is Good Friday?"

"Do not chide me that I did not know," begged Peredur. "For it is many months since I left my own country, and in all that time I have seen neither churches nor holy men."

He dismounted and took off his armour, and loaded it on his horse, and walked beside the priest, leading his horse, till they came to a hermitage.

"Tarry with me here over Eastertide," said the priest.

And this Peredur did.

When Eastertide was over, and Peredur was preparing to depart, he told the priest that he was in search of the way to the Castle of Wonders.

"On the other side of that mountain yonder," replied the priest, "there is a valley, and in that valley there is a town, and in that town there is a royal palace. There the King of these parts comes with his Court to keep Easter. There, if anywhere, will you hear tidings of this Castle of Wonders."

So Peredur rode forward, with the priest's blessing. Beyond the mountain he went down into the valley; and there he met the King and his Court, out hunting.

They exchanged courteous greetings. Then the King called to him a little yellow page, and said:

"Guide this knight to my palace, and bid my daughter entertain him well till I return."

The little yellow page guided Peredur to the palace, where the princess welcomed him, and helped him to unarm, and brought him fresh garments. It seemed to the page that the princess and Peredur took too much pleasure in each other's company. This he reported to the King on his return; and the King, enraged, had Peredur seized and cast into a dungeon.

When the princess heard of this, she went to Peredur there.

"Is it unpleasant to you to be here?" she asked.

"I should not mind if I were not," he answered.

"If you will pledge your faith to return at night," she told him, "I will set you free by day."

Just then they heard a tumult in the town.

"What is that tumult?" Peredur asked.

"It is a powerful Earl," the princess told him, "who has come with all his men to attack my father."

"Give me my horse and arms," said Peredur, "and I will go to your father's aid, and return here afterwards."

The princess caused his horse and arms to be brought to him, together with a yellow shield and a scarlet robe to wear over his armour. In this disguise, Peredur rode out to the combat, where he fought valiantly all day; and in the evening, when the fighting ceased, he returned to his dungeon.

As the King sat at meat that night with his daughter, she asked:

"My father, which of your household acquitted himself best to-day?"

"No-one of my household," he told her, "but a stranger, a knight wearing a scarlet robe and bearing a yellow shield."

At daybreak, when fighting was resumed, Peredur went out again to the combat-again he fought valiantly all day, and when night fell he returned to his dungeon.

That night, as the princess and her father again sat at meat, she asked him:

"Father, who acquitted himself best today?"

"Again the unknown knight," he told her.

"Did you not discover who he was?" she asked.

"When I sent my heralds to enquire," said the King, "he was nowhere to be found."

On the third day of fighting, Peredur slew the Earl himself, and again returned to his dungeon.

"I have good news for you, daughter," said the King that night. "The Earl is slain, and I now possess his Earldom."

"Who slew him?" asked the princess.

"The unknown knight," said the King.

"Father," said the princess, "he is unknown to you, but he is not unknown to me. He is the knight whom you have wrongfully imprisoned."

Then the King sent to free Peredur, and had him brought to sit with him at meat. He thanked him, and begged his forgiveness, and bade him ask what he would, even to his daughter's hand and half his kingdom.

"I came not here to woo," said Peredur, "but to seek tidings of the way to the Castle of Wonders."

"Such tidings are easily told," said the King. "Beyond the next mountain there is a lake, and in that lake there is an island, and on that island there is a castle, and that castle is the Castle of Wonders."

"Yet you would be wiser not to go there," said the princess.

"Go there I must," said Peredur, "and for two reasons. One is that I must go through it to learn the meaning of the bleeding spear. And the other is that through it lies the way to the castle where I must keep tryst with the knight whom I love best in the world."

"They are both good reasons," said the King. "Tarry this night with us here; and tomorrow I will send my chief huntsman with you, to guide you to the lake."

So Peredur tarried the night; and that night it was in no dungeon that he slept, but in a pleasant chamber. And next morning he exchanged farewells with the King and the princess, and rode forward, with the King's chief huntsman as guide, on the last part of his way to the Castle of Wonders.

XII. HOW PEREDUR CAME TO THE CASTLE OF WONDERS

HEN Peredur came over the mountain pass with the King's huntsman, he saw below him a great lake spreading like the sea, and in the lake an island, and a castle on its shore. They rode steeply down to the lake, and the huntsman led Peredur to where a boat was hidden among the reeds.

"Lord," he said, "this boat will take you to the island without oars and without sails."

Peredur led his horse into the boat, and at once they began to float across the water. When the huntsman saw that all was well, he turned and rode back towards the mountain pass.

When the boat reached the island, Peredur led his horse ashore. He mounted him, and rode along the water's edge to the castle. The gate of the castle was open, and he rode through. When he reached the door of the hall, that also was open; and that also he rode through.

There was no-one in the hall. He dismounted and went to the window, and he saw how, below, the lake lapped the castle walls. Behind him he heard shouting, and turned quickly. Still there was no-one in the hall; but he saw that a chessboard with squares of ebony and ivory lay on the great table, and that set out on it were chessmen of gold and of silver, and that these chessmen were playing against each other, with no hand moving them.

Peredur went to watch the game. He said to himself:

"I favour the golden side."

But the golden side lost; and the silver side shouted again as if they had been living men.

At this Peredur was so angry that he opened the window by its ivory pin, and cast both board and chessmen down into the lake. Behind him he heard a scornful laugh; he turned, and there stood the black maiden he had seen at King Arthur's Court.

"Ah, Peredur!" she cried. "Always you do evil!"

"What new evil have I done?" he asked.

"You have thrown the Empress's chessboard into the lake," she said, "and she prizes it above all things."

"Is there no way to recover it?" he asked.

"In the Castle of Ysbidinongyl," she said, "dwells a black man who lays waste this land. If you can slay him, the chessboard will return to its own place. But *he* is more likely to slay *you*."

"Where lies this castle?" Peredur asked.

The black maiden led him to the door, and pointed out the track which led to the castle. As Peredur rode towards it, the black man rode out to meet him. They fought till the black man was overthrown and begged for mercy.

"Mercy you shall have," said Peredur, "on one condition: that you place the chessboard of the Empress back in its own place."

36   "This I have done already," said the black man.

So Peredur granted him his life, and rode back to the Castle of Wonders. The black maiden stood at the door.

"The chessboard is *not* back in its place," she cried. "You did not slay that monster. If you would make your peace with the Empress, go back and slay him now."

So this Peredur did.

When he returned again to the Castle of Wonders, the chessboard was back in its place. But the black maiden said:

"You have still a second deed to do, and that is to behead the stag which runs wild in the Empress's forest."

"How shall I find him?" asked Peredur.

"The Empress's little dog," she said, "will rouse him and drive him towards you."

She called the little dog, who guided Peredur into the forest, then roused the stag and drove him towards Peredur. Peredur let the stag run past him, and, as he did so, smote off his head with his sword.

Then he saw that around the neck of the stag there was a golden collar. As he dismounted to examine it, the little dog set up a joyful barking, and, glancing up, Peredur saw a lady riding towards him.

"Alas!" she cried, as she saw the beheaded stag. "You have slain the creature I loved best in all the world."

"Lady, how may I make my peace?" asked Peredur.

"Go towards the lake," she said, pointing. "You will come to a grove, and in the grove a cromlech. Call out a challenge three times, and fight whoever answers it."

Peredur rode towards the lake. He came to the grove, and drew rein beside the cromlech; and three times he called out his challenge.

Then out of the cromlech came a black man in rusty armour, riding a bony horse. They fought, and Peredur overthrew him. But no sooner had he touched the ground than he was seated again in his saddle. A second time Peredur overthrew him, and again no sooner was he thrown than he was seated again in his saddle. A third time Peredur overthrew him, and in the same moment leapt from his own horse, sword in hand, to fight on foot.

But already the black man was seated again in his saddle. He caught up the rein of Peredur's horse; and together with both horses he vanished into thin air.

XIII. HOW PEREDUR CAME AGAIN TO THE CASTLE OF HIS UNCLE

THEN Peredur looked about him; and beside the lake he saw a castle. He went towards it. When he came to the gate, it was open; so he went through it. When he came to the door of the hall, that, too, was open; so he went through that.

In the hall sat a kingly old man with white hair, with a younger man beside him. And he knew the one for his lame uncle, and the other for Gawain.

They greeted each other with joy, and Peredur sat down beside them. Looking about him, he saw his horse, which the black man had taken, standing quietly beside Gawain's. Then a yellow-haired youth came in, and went down on his knee before him.

"Lord," he said, "it was I who came to you in the guise of a black maiden at King Arthur's Court and in the Castle of Wonders. But before that, here in my father's hall, you saw me bear in the bleeding spear. For I will not conceal from you that I am your cousin, and that the head borne in by the two maidens was my brother's."

"Who slew your brother?" asked Peredur.

"The Nine Sorceresses of Gloucester," the youth told him. "It was they also who lamed my father. But it is foretold that Goodly Peredur will right these wrongs."

Then Peredur and Gawain took counsel together; and their decision was to ask King Arthur and his household to go with them against the sorceresses. So they rode back together to King Arthur's Court to enlist his aid.

And when, with King Arthur's aid, the land had been cleansed of the evil wrought by the sorceresses and the lame King had been healed, Peredur returned to King Arthur's Court; and Queen Guinevere and Angarad received him joyfully. And there, till further adventures drove him forth, he dwelt in the fellowship of King Arthur's knights in great content.

THE LADY OF THE FOUNTAIN

THE LADY OF THE FOUNTAIN

I. HOW SIR KYNON CAME TO THE FOUNTAIN

SIR KYNON set out one day from King Arthur's Court in search of adventure. He rode till he came to a great forest; and in the forest he found a track which ran beside a river. He followed the track till it came out of the forest and crossed a wide plain; and there, at the far edge of the plain, stood a castle, shining in the sun.

As he drew near to the castle, a noble old man in a yellow mantle came to meet him, and brought him courteously into the castle hall. Here four and twenty of the fairest maidens he had ever seen were sitting at their needlework, on chairs of gold beneath a great window of painted glass. They rose to welcome him; they took his horse and armour; they brought him fresh garments, and a silver bowl in which to wash; they spread a long table with white linen and with vessels of gold and silver, and set meat and wine on it.

When they had all eaten and drunk together, the old man asked Sir Kynon:

"Sir, what is your name, and what do you ride in search of?"

Sir Kynon told him his name, and that he rode in search of any knight who could master him in feats of arms.

Then the old man said, smiling:

"Sleep here tonight; and tomorrow I will set you on your way to what you seek."

So Sir Kynon slept that night in the castle; and early next morning, when he was armed and mounted, the old man directed him:

"Ride back across the plain and into the forest as far as the first crossroad. There take the path which branches to the right. It will lead you to a mound, on which sits the woodward of the forest. He will direct you further."

Sir Kynon did as the old man had bidden him. When he came to the mound, on it was sitting a black giant, with only one foot and one eye, and with a huge iron club in his hand; deer and dragons and every sort of wild animal grazed quietly around him.

"Sir," said Sir Kynon, "I am in search of any knight who can master me in feats of arms."

"Follow this path," said the giant, "till you come to an open glade with a single green tree in the midst of it. Under this tree you will find a fountain with a marble slab beside it; chained to the marble slab you will find a silver bowl. Fill the bowl at the fountain, and cast the water over the slab. If you do not find there the knight you seek, you will find him nowhere in the world.''

Sir Kynon thanked the black giant and rode forward; and presently he came to the fountain. He dismounted, and filled the bowl, and cast the water over the slab; and at once the whole forest shook with peal after peal of thunder.

Scarcely had he re-mounted his horse when there came a storm of hailstones, cutting through armour and flesh to the very bone. He held the beak of his shield over his horse's head and its upper part over his own till the hailstones ceased. By then there was not one leaf left clinging to the tree.

Then the sky grew bright and clear; and birds came flying, and settled on the tree till its stripped branches were covered with them. And never had Sir Kynon heard melody as sweet as those birds sang.

Then into the glade there charged a knight, on a powerful jet-black steed. A black pennon streamed from his lance, and over his armour he wore a robe of black velvet. So sudden and so furious was his onset that though Sir Kynon was skilled in arms, he was instantly overthrown.

The Black Knight paid no further heed to him. Slipping his lance-head through the bridle-rein of Sir Kynon's charger, he galloped back with him into the forest, leaving Sir Kynon lying where he had fallen.

Then Sir Kynon, shaken but not wounded, rose and went slowly back towards the mound on his two feet, weighed down by his armour. At his coming, the black giant laughed so loudly that Sir Kynon could have died for very shame. But on he went till he reached the crossroads; then on again till he reached the plain, and rejoiced to see again, at its far edge, the castle shining in the sun.

Again the old nobleman in his yellow mantle came to meet him. Again the four and twenty maidens rose from their needlework to welcome him and array him in fresh garments. Again they all ate and drank together, in the same friendliness and good fellowship. But not one word was spoken, nor any question asked, concerning Sir Kynon's adventure.

He slept again at the castle; and when, next morning, his host bade him Godspeed, he gave him a noble palfrey on which to ride away. Back to King Arthur's Court Sir Kynon rode; and King Arthur rejoiced at his coming. To the King and the Court Sir Kynon told the story of all his other adventures; but the story of his adventure at the fountain he kept locked in his own breast.

II.   HOW KING ARTHUR SLEPT BEFORE SUPPER

O NE evening, King Arthur was sitting in his chamber, waiting for the supper-horn to blow. At his feet, on red and yellow cushions, sat Sir Kynon, with Sir Owain, who was one of the King's nephews, and with Sir Kay of the Wry Tongue, who was Steward of the Royal Household. In the great painted window sat Queen Guinevere and her ladies, working with their needles at their coloured tapestry.

Presently King Arthur said:

"I think I will sleep a little. Kynon and Owain, think of a good tale to tell Kay, and he will give you a goblet of mead and a skewer of collops to keep you alive till supper."

And he leaned his head on his hand and closed his eyes.

"Kay," said Sir Kynon, "give us what the King promised us."

"First," said Sir Kay, "give me what the King promised *me*."

"When you have fed us," said Sir Owain, "we will tell you the best tale we know."

Then from the mead-cellar Sir Kay fetched a goblet of mead, and from the kitchen a handful of skewers packed with broiled collops of venison. When they had eaten and drunk, he said:

"And now give me my story."

"Kynon," said Sir Owain, "*you* give Kay his story."

"Owain," replied Sir Kynon, "you are a better teller of tales than I."

"But you have seen more of the world," said Sir Owain. "Tell us of the strangest thing that ever befell you."

Sir Kynon looked at Queen Guinevere and her ladies at their needlework beneath the painted window, and they brought to his mind the four and twenty maidens seated at their needlework beneath that other painted window in the castle on the plain.

"I will do so," he said.

And he told them the story of his adventure at the fountain.

"Kay," he ended, "I think no knight ever before told of an adventure so much to his shame. It is strange that only I, of all the king's knights, have encountered it."

"I would that *I* might!" cried Sir Owain.

"Deeds speak louder than words," snapped Sir Kay.

At that moment the supper horn was sounded; and King Arthur stirred and opened his eyes.

"Was I sleeping a little?" he asked.

"A little, Sire," said Owain.

But it was indeed so little that Sir Kynon's story was interwoven with the King's dreams.

They washed their hands, and went out into the hall; and all the King's household gathered there and sat down to eat together. And afterwards they passed the evening in talk and games and minstrelsy. But all the time Sir Owain sat silent and withdrawn.

For Sir Kynon's story had roused in him the desire to seek the adventure of the fountain, and Sir Kay's scoffing comment had hardened his resolve.

So, when he went that night to his lodging, he made all ready to depart secretly at dawn; and so, next morning, nowhere in King Arthur's palace was Sir Owain to be found.

III.   HOW SIR OWAIN CAME TO THE FOUNTAIN

SIR OWAIN followed the path traced out for him by Sir Kynon's story. He rode till he reached the great forest, and in it he found the track which ran beside the river. He followed the track till it came out of the forest and crossed the wide plain; and there, at the far edge of the plain, he saw the castle, shining in the sun.

The noble old man of Sir Kynon's story came to meet him. In the hall the four and twenty fair maidens of Sir Kynon's story welcomed him. And when they had eaten and drunk together, his host asked him the same question:

"Sir, what is your name, and what do you ride in search of?"

Sir Owain told him his name, and that he rode in search of the knight who guarded the fountain.

And the old man said, smiling, as he had said to Sir Kynon:

"Sleep here tonight; and tomorrow I will set you on your way to him."

Next morning he directed Sir Owain to the black woodward on the mound; and the black woodward directed him further to the glade with the single green tree, and, under it, the fountain. Here Sir Owain brimmed the silver bowl, and cast the water over the marble slab; and all happened with him as with Sir Kynon — the thunder, the hailstorm, the stripping of the tree, the flocking of the birds, their enchanted melody.

But where Sir Kynon had been unprepared for what came next, Sir Owain was forewarned by his story.

So, when the Black Knight burst into the glade, Sir Owain was ready to meet him. So violent was their encounter that both their lances splintered. Now they fought blade to blade; and Sir Owain's sword split the Black Knight's helmet, and pierced both flesh and bone.

The Black Knight fell forward on his black steed's neck; and the steed turned and bore him swiftly home. Sir Owain pursued him as swiftly; and suddenly they were out of the forest, and Sir Owain saw before him a great castle, and, within its surrounding walls, stately pinnacles and the many roofs of a clustering town.

The gate of the city was flung wide for the black steed and his burden to enter. Then, as Sir Owain made to follow, the portcullis fell like a guillotine. It cut his horse in two behind the saddle and even sliced the rowels from his spurs. The portcullis was down; the inner gate was shut fast; and there was Sir Owain, caught between them.

Through the grill in the inner gate, he could see a steep street of houses; and along it came a maiden with curling yellow hair.

"I pray you, open the gate," she said through the grill.

"Lady," said Sir Owain, "Heaven knows this is no more in my power than it is in yours to set me free."

"We will see about that," she said. "They are coming to put you to death. But they will find nothing but half your horse if you will hold your hand under the grill."

Sir Owain did so. She pushed something small and bright through the grill. It fell on his open palm; and he saw that it was a ring.

"Put it on your finger, with the stone turned inside your hand," she said. "Close your hand over the stone. As long as you hide the stone, the stone will hide *you*."

"And then?" he asked.

"They will open the gate and you will slip out while they stand agape," she told him. "I will be waiting by the horse-block. You will see *me*, but *I* shall not see *you*. So lay your hand on my shoulder; and where I go, go with me."

She slipped away as men-at-arms came clanking over the cobbles. They opened the gate, calling on the knight beyond it to yield. But they found no knight beyond it.

For Sir Owain, with his hand closed over the stone in the ring, had slipped through the gate as they opened it. He had joined the maiden waiting by the horse-block. He had laid his hand on her shoulder. And now, while the men-at-arms searched and searched again the space between the gate and the portcullis, the maiden was quietly moving along a side-street; and as quietly, and most thankfully, the invisible Sir Owain was moving with her.

IV.   HOW LUNED HID SIR OWAIN

PRESENTLY the maiden paused at a closed door. She unlocked it and drew Sir Owain in, then closed and locked it again. He found himself in a large and most beautiful chamber, richly painted and adorned with golden images.

"Now turn the ring," she said, "that as you see *me*, so may I see *you*."

Sir Owain turned the ring so that its jewel shone outwards. The maiden set a stool beside the fire for him, and brought water in a silver bowl that he might wash. She helped him to unarm, and arrayed him in fresh garments. Then she set meat and drink before him; and as he ate, he asked:

"Lady, what is your name?"

"Luned, Sir Owain," she replied.

"You know me?" he asked, amazed.

"I saw you," she said, "when the Countess whom I serve sent me on a mission to King Arthur's Court."

"Luned," he said, "I owe my life to you. How now can I serve *you*?"

"By serving the Countess whom *I* serve," she said. "She is the lady of this castle, and soon she will be in dire need of a faithful knight's service."

Faintly they heard the sound of distant chanting.

"What is that chanting?" he asked.

"It is the priests," she said, "chanting around the bed of the lord of this castle, who is near to death."

She made ready a couch for him, of costly furs without, and of fine white linen within.

"Sleep," she said, "and I will watch over your sleep."

He slept. But at midnight he was awakened by the sound of wailing. By the light of a tall candle, he could see Luned sitting on a stool beside his couch, watching over him.

"What is that wailing?" he asked.

"They are mourning the death of the lord of the castle," she said. "Sleep again. Tomorrow there will be work for you to do."

Again he slept. But in the dark time before dawn he was again awakened, this time by the marching of many feet.

"What is that marching?" he asked.

"They are bearing to church," she said, "the body of the lord of the castle."

Then Sir Owain rose, and cast a robe about him, and opened the window of the chamber, and leaned out. All the way up the hill to the castle, the darkness was alive with torches, and the streets were filled from wall to wall with people, riding and on foot. The torchlight was leaping on armour, and its shadows were leaping high and low on the walls.

Now came singing priests, and in their midst a bier. It was covered with a pall of purple velvet, and all about it flickered the flames of waxen tapers.

Behind the bier rode a lady, weeping sorely. Her beauty was marred by her sorrow; yet the moment Sir Owain saw her, he loved her with his whole heart.

"Who is she?" he asked.

"She is my mistress, the Countess Aluntine," she told him. "She is the lady of this castle, and she is also called the Lady of the Fountain."

"Of all the ladies in the world," he said, "she is the lady I love best."

"That is well," said Luned drily. "For it is you who must serve and protect her now, since it is you who have made her a widow."

"I?" cried Sir Owain.

"Do you not understand?" said Luned. "The body on that bier is the body of Sir Salados, who became the lord of her two castles when he wedded her. He was the protector and defender of her two Earldoms. It was he who died at midnight; and he died of the mortal wound you gave him at the Fountain."

This news smote Sir Owain silent. Bitterly he regretted for the lady's sake that he had ever come in search of the Adventure of the Fountain. Yet never to have done so would have meant never to have seen her.

At last he humbly asked:

"How can I serve her?"

"By taking the place of Sir Salados," she said.

"Gladly would I do so," said Sir Owain, "if this should be her will."

Luned kindled the fire again, and set food before him.

"Stay hidden a little longer," she said, "while I go and do your wooing."

Then she went out, locking the door behind her, and climbed the steep street to the castle.

V. HOW LUNED DID SIR OWAIN'S WOOING

HEN Luned reached the castle, the Lady of the Fountain had returned from the church, and was alone in her chamber, weeping.

Luned entered and greeted her; but the Countess wept on, and did not return her greeting.

"My Lady Aluntine," said Luned, "are you answering no-one today?"

"Luned," said the Countess, "have you no respect for my grief for the loss of that brave knight who defended the Fountain?" "I would have more," replied Luned, bluntly, "were you to bestir yourself to fill his place."

"How can you speak so, with Sir Salados not yet cold?" cried the Countess. "Luned, go from my presence!"

Luned went as far as the door of the chamber. Then she turned and said:

"It is a pity that you send from you one who could have helped you in this matter."

She swept through the door. But outside, at the top of the stone corkscrew stairs, she paused and waited.

For at her last words the Countess had ceased weeping and looked up; and now she rose, and followed Luned, and coughed to draw her attention. Then she opened the door, and beckoned, and went back into her chamber. Luned, smiling to herself, respectfully followed her in.

"You have an evil disposition, Luned," said the Countess. "But if you *can* help me in this matter, tell me how."

"My Lady Aluntine," said Luned, "in these lawless days a lady who has two Earldoms has no choice but to wed a strong knight to defend them for her. Is this not so?"

"Alas, it is so," sighed the Countess.

"And if the knight she has wed is slain," went on Luned, "she has no choice but to take another in his place. Is that not so?"

"Alas, it is so," sighed the Countess again.

"The Knights of King Arthur's Court are the best in all the world, said Luned. "Is that not so?"

"Indeed, it is so," agreed the Countess.

"You have already sent me on one mission to that Court," went on Luned. "Is that not so?"

"It is even so," said the Countess.

"Then send me now on another," said Luned.

The Countess thought awhile.

"This I will do," she decided.

So Luned set out as if to go on this mission. By daylight she rode out through the city gate; but by night she stole back through a postern, and came secretly to the house in which she had lodged Sir Owain. And there she lay low for as long as it would have taken her to ride to King Arthur's Court and back to the castle again.

The Countess welcomed her warmly, and asked eagerly what tidings she brought. "The best of tidings," said Luned. "Is it your will that I present to you a knight of King Arthur's Court, young, brave, comely, most skilled in feats of arms, most faithful in his service of ladies in distress?"

"Bring him to my chamber tomorrow at noon," said the Countess.

Next day at noon Luned brought Sir Owain to the castle, clad in a new surcoat and mantle of yellow satin, adorned with golden lace. And when the Countess Aluntine received him in her chamber, it seemed to her that he was indeed all that Luned had said, and her grief was lightened at his coming.

"Tomorrow," she said, "I will cause all the high-born vassals of both my Earldoms to assemble. I will place this matter before them; and by their counsel I will abide."

When her vassals were assembled, she said to them:

"Well do you know how the death of Sir Salados has left our two Earldoms open to war and invasion unless and until I wed another Guardian of the Fountain. So now I would have you choose and for ever abide by your choice – either that one of yourselves should wed me, or that with your consent I wed this knight of King Arthur's Court and you accept him as your lord."

Now the vassals of neither of her Earldoms were willing to accept as their lord a vassal of the other Earldom. They all had rather that she should wed the knight of King Arthur's Court. So to this they gave their consent, and pledged their faith to accept him as their lord.

So the Countess Aluntine was married to Sir Owain by the Bishop of the city, and all the vassals of both her Earldoms did homage to their new lord. For three years Sir Owain, clad in black velvet, like Sir Salados before him, defended the Fountain, and was never once defeated. And, under his overlordship, during all that time the Countess Aluntine's two Earldoms prospered and were at peace.

VI. HOW KING ARTHUR CAME TO THE FOUNTAIN

AT the close of those three years, Sir Gawain was walking in the Tilting Meadow with King Arthur one day, and it seemed to him that the King was very sad. Now Sir Gawain was not only one of King Arthur's knights; he was also one of his nephews. So now he asked:

"Uncle, why are you so sorrowful?"

King Arthur answered, sighing:

"There is another who has not called me 'Uncle' for three years. It is three years since I lost your cousin Owain. Sometimes I think he is slain; sometimes I think he is a captive. For if he is neither, he has surely forgotten me."

Then Gawain said, using his golden tongue to lighten King Arthur's sorrow:

"Uncle, I will go and find him for you. If he is slain, I will avenge him. If he is a captive, I will set him free. If he is alive, I will bring him back to you."

"I will go with you," said the King.

"On what adventure was he bent?" asked Sir Gawain.

"I do not know," said the King. "He departed secretly by night. It was the night, I call to mind, that Kynon told of his Adventure at the Fountain. Now I am sure it was through that tale that I lost Owain."

And he told Sir Gawain the story of the evening he had slept before supper.

"Then Kynon shall come with us and be our guide," said Sir Gawain.

When Sir Kay heard what was afoot, he insisted on going with them.

"For that was *my* tale," he said. "Kynon told it in payment for my mead and collops."

So the King and the three knights set out with their attendants. Sir Kynon led them to the great forest; and through the forest to the plain; and across the plain to the castle shining in the sun.

Here the old nobleman met them, and the four and twenty maidens welcomed them; and after they had eaten, they slept that night in the castle.

Next morning Sir Kynon led them to the mound, on which sat the black giant, and past it to the glade with its single green tree, with the fountain beneath it.

As King Arthur reined in his horse, to gaze at the marble slab and the silver bowl chained beside it, Sir Kay rode forward, crying:

"Sire, grant me the first adventure."

"I grant it, Kay," said the King.

Then Sir Kay brimmed the bowl and dashed the water over the marble slab; and all happened as in Sir Kynon's first recounting. First came the thunder, and after the thunder, hail; and after the hail, sweet birdsong from the leafless tree; and then, suddenly, a knight clad in black velvet bearing down on Sir Kay, riding a mettlesome black steed.

Sir Kay was the finest horseman in all King Arthur's Court; but he could not withstand that fierce encounter. He was instantly overthrown; and the Black Knight galloped swiftly away, and Sir Kay's charger with him.

They camped that night near the fountain; and the next day Sir Kynon also was overthrown. The third day was Sir Gawain's.

So fierce was the encounter between him and the Black Knight that their lances splintered and they were both unhorsed. Both rose and drew their swords and continued to fight on foot. A sword-thrust of the Black Knight's opened Sir Gawain's visor. The other knight halted in mid-stroke; then he unhelmed, and opened his arms; and with cries of "Owain!" and "Gawain!" the two cousins embraced each other.

Then King Arthur, marvelling, came forward and joyfully embraced his long-lost nephew; and Sir Owain brought them all to the Countess Aluntine's castle; and here they feasted and made merry till King Arthur's thoughts turned homewards.

Then the King begged a boon of Aluntine – that Sir Owain might return with him to his Court for three months. She granted the boon, though a pang went through her heart.

And Sir Owain said farewell to his wife, and rode away to King Arthur's Court with the King and his old companions.

VII.   HOW SIR OWAIN LOST HIMSELF

IR OWAIN'S three months at King Arthur's Court grew into six, then into a year, then into two years, then into three. At the end of the third year, he was sitting one day at meat with the King and his household when a maiden rode into the hall. She was clothed in yellow satin, and her palfrey was bathed in foam.

She drew rein before Sir Owain, and drew his wedding ring from his finger, and cast it on the table before him.

"Thus shall be treated," she said, "all who do not keep faith."

Then she turned her palfrey, and spurred him from the hall.

Then all those earlier three years with the Countess Aluntine, which had faded to a dream, came back to Sir Owain; and he knew that the maiden had spoken truly when she said he had not kept faith. When he went that night to his lodging, he made all ready to depart secretly at dawn, as he had done before.

And, as before, next morning nowhere in King Arthur's palace was Sir Owain to be found.

As before, he rode till he reached the great forest. But search as he would, he could not this time find the track that ran by the river and out to the plain, nor the path that branched from it and led past the black giant's mound to the fountain, and then onwards to the Countess's castle. Instead, he lost himself in the forest, and there his wits went astray.

His horse ran from him, laden with his armour. What garments he was left with soon wore to rags, and in time dropped clean away. His naked body grew gaunt and wasted; his nails and hair and beard grew long; he lived with, and like, the wild beasts.

At last even they cast him out, for he had grown too weak to fight for food, too weak to wander with them. He crawled alone down a valley to drink from a lake, and fainted on its shore.

Now, there was a young Earl, named Sir Alers, whose lands bordered those of the Countess. When Sir Owain had failed to return to guard the Fountain, this young Earl had tried to force her to become his wife; and when she refused, he had made war on her, and had taken from her the greater of her two Earldoms, together with the larger of her castles, in which, with its city, she had always dwelt. So now, with only a few attendants, she dwelt in her smaller castle, which stood near this same lake.

One day she and one of her maidens were walking beside the lake when they came upon the naked body of a man. He seemed to be a wild man of the woods.

When she had laid her hand upon his heart, she said:

"There is a little life still in him, if we can but save the spark."

So they hastened back to the little castle; and from her coffer the Countess took a flask of precious balsam. It had been a gift from King Arthur's chief physician, Morgant the Wise.

"Hasten back with this," she said to the maiden. "Anoint the wild man with it about his heart. I will send a steed after you, and garments. Watch over him, and when he revives, bring him to the castle."

The maiden returned to Sir Owain with the balsam, and emptied the whole flask over him. She sat down to watch beside him, and presently a second maiden appeared, bringing a steed, with garments laid over the saddle. As they tethered the steed to a tree, Sir Owain sighed deeply and began to stir.

The two maidens took the garments from the saddle, and with their aid he put them on. Then they helped him to mount the steed, and, holding him steady, one on each side, they brought him to the castle, and laid him on a couch, lapped in cool linen, and kindled a fire, and warmed broth for him to drink.

There they cared for him till he was strong again; but his mind was not yet fully restored. He did not know his wife; to him she was a kind stranger, the mistress of a castle he had never seen before. And since he himself still bore the marks of his forest wildness, neither did she know him.

One day three months after his coming, Sir Owain awoke one dawn to sounds of tumult. He rose, and opened his window, and looked down on a host of men so great that he could not see its ending. Their leader, a knight in richly gilded armour, stood with his trumpeters before the castle gate.

At Sir Owain's call, one of the maidens who tended him entered, wringing her hands.

"It is Sir Alers," she told him, "the Earl who has already taken my mistress's greater Earldom from her; and now he comes to take the smaller one, also."

"Get me a horse and arms," he said.

The maiden came to the Countess, and told her of the wild man's request. In the midst of all her woes, Aluntine laughed.

"Let him have them," she said, "though I know not what he would do with them."

Sir Owain put on the armour, and mounted the horse, and rode out to the gate. He ordered it to be opened, and beckoned to Sir Alers. The young Earl rode forward.

All the rules of chivalry had gone clean out of the sick knight's head. He snatched Sir Alers out of his saddle, and, backing his own steed, pulled the young Earl through the portal. The portcullis fell with a clang. Sir Alers was a prisoner, cut off from all his men.

Sir Owain brought him straight to the chamber of the Countess.

"Madam, I bring you my return for your balsam," he said. "To ransom his life, let Sir Alers render you back your Earldom and swear fealty as your man. The army he has brought against you let him maintain here to serve you."

All this Sir Alers promised to do. And all this he did.

When all was concluded, Sir Owain thanked the Countess and her maidens for their care of him, called again for the steed she had given him, and rode out alone into a world in which he was still a stranger.

VIII.   HOW SIR OWAIN FOUND HIMSELF

AS SIR OWAIN rode deeper into the forest, he heard a lion roaring. Presently he came to a mound, on which was a great serpent, lurking within a cleft rock. A black lion stood near the rock; every time he attempted to escape, the great serpent darted at him, hissing, and drove him back again.

Sir Owain unsheathed his sword as he drew near; as the serpent darted out, he bent from his saddle, cutting the serpent in two. As he rode on, the lion came leaping after him, fawning on him and frisking about him like a happy puppy.

In this way they went on through the forest, until, as evening began to draw on, they came to a flat meadow, and here Sir Owain turned his horse loose. He kindled a fire, for which the lion brought fuel. The lion then went hunting, and presently returned to lay a fine roebuck at Sir Owain's feet.

Sir Owain skinned the roebuck, and made skewers of stripped twigs, and packed them with collops of venison, and gave the rest of the roebuck to the lion. He laid the collops about the fire to broil; and as he sat watching them, it seemed to him that he heard a deep sigh behind him. He looked, but could see no-one. A second sigh he heard, and then a third.

"Is there a mortal near?" he called aloud.

A faint voice answered him.

"Who speaks?" he called again.

Again the faint voice answered:

"I am named Luned."

"Where are you?" he called a third time.

And a third time the faint voice answered:

"I am imprisoned in this vault."

Sir Owain searched all about, and found the vault, but he could find no way in. "How can I release you?" he asked.

"Only those who put me in know how to get me out," replied the voice. "They are two false knights, of whom I said that my lord is more than a match for both. They have sworn to burn me if he does not come to prove my words."

"And why has he not done so?" asked Sir Owain.

"Alas," said the maiden, "he is at King Arthur's Court, and knows nothing of my plight; and the day they have set for the combat is the day after tomorrow."

"If he is not here by then," promised Sir Owain, "I will fight them in his place."

When the collops were ready, he took them from the fire; and she told him of a gap between the stones through which food could be passed. So in the dusk they ate together, she within the vault, and he without.

They talked all through the night; and at dawn he asked if there was a castle near, where he could spend the following night and be back in the meadow in time for the next day's combat; and she told him of such a castle on the other side of the river, which he could reach by the next ford.

So he and the lion departed, and came to the ford, and crossed it, and so came to the castle. A noble Earl clothed all in black brought him into the hall. The lion at first went with Sir Owain's steed, and lay down in his manger; but when the folk of the castle sat down to meat, the lion came and lay at Sir Owain's feet, and ate of all that he ate.

Sir Owain was seated between the Earl and his most lovely daughter; she also was all in black, and both were as sorrowful as death. Sir Owain looked about the hall, and saw that all the folk of the castle also were in black, and also all as sorrowful as death. At last he could contain himself no longer, but said to the Earl:

"Lord, what is the cause of all this heavy cheer?"

"I will tell you," the Earl answered. "A savage giant dwells nearby, called Harpyn of the Mountain. He has my two sons captive; and today he brings them to exchange them for my daughter. And unless I deliver her up to him, he will slay my sons before my eyes."

Even as he spoke, a great tumult arose without, and the servingmen came running with the news:

"Lord! Lord! Harpyn the Giant is at the gate!"

"I will go forth to him," said Sir Owain.

Sir Owain donned his armour, the Earl's daughter aiding him. Then he rode out to meet the giant, and the lion ran at his heels.

The giant was as tall as two men; he was clothed in bull-skins, and in one hand he brandished a great iron club, while with the other he dragged by a chain the Earl's two sons. When he saw Sir Owain riding forth, he let out a roar, and strode to meet him with his club upraised. It was not easy for Sir Owain to fight him without harming his two captives. But the lion, with a roar which matched the giant's own, launched himself upon him. With one stroke of his paw he laid his heart bare, and the giant fell down dead.

Great were the rejoicings in the castle that night. Early next morning, Sir Owain took his leave, and rode back to the place of combat. But early as he was, the two false knights were before him. Already they had kindled the fire for Luned's burning. Already they had taken her from the vault, and were dragging her to the flames.

But when they heard Sir Owain bearing down upon them, they loosed their hold on Luned, drew their swords, and fell upon him. But if Sir Owain fought back fiercely, so did the lion beside him. Two blows of his paw, like the one he gave to Harpyn, and both false knights, like Harpyn, fell down dead.

Then Luned came running, crying:

"With my whole heart I thank you, Sir Owain."

And as soon as he heard his own name, Sir Owain found himself again. He remembered who he was; he remembered his wife Aluntine. Joyfully he returned with Luned to her; and as joyfully Aluntine received them. And from then on, Sir Owain and his Lady of the Fountain dwelt in great love together as long as they both lived.

MARIE de FRANCE
AND HER
BRETON LAYS

MARIE DE FRANCE AND HER 12TH. CENTURY BRETON LAYS

THE BRETONS, as their name suggests, were of the same racial stock as the Britons. (In medieval Latin the Bretons were *Britones* and the Britons were *Britanni*). So, when England was conquered by the Anglo-Saxons, while some of the defeated Britons, as we have seen, took refuge with their brother Celts in Wales and Cornwall, others crossed the sea to Brittany, then known as Little Britain, taking their stories of King Arthur with them.

There these Arthurian stories received fresh life-blood; the Breton storytellers forged a new medieval form for them – the Breton lay, less rugged, more beautiful, in rhymed verse, much shorter than the ancient form, and often with a charming fairy-tale quality.

In this form the Arthurian stories were received with delight not only in other parts of France but also in other countries; they became the seeds of a whole new medieval literature in Europe.

Meanwhile, in the year 1066, the Anglo-Saxons who, in the fifth and sixth centuries, had invaded and conquered the Britons, were now themselves invaded and conquered by the Normans. The Normans brought with them French influences, and presently there appeared among these the new forms of troubadour poetry, of chivalry and of courtly love, in which the Arthurian ideals were now seeking expression on the Continent.

When, in the year 1154, Henry of Anjou became King of England, his wife, Eleanor of Aquitaine, made the Anglo-Norman court a centre of these new ideals. Some scholars say that among the poets who wrote and sang there was Marie de France, and that she was the half-sister of the King. She was the most famous woman minstrel of the twelfth century.

Our next story, *The Lay of Sir Lanval,* is a Breton lay which she had heard a Breton bard singing in his own dialect, and which she had so greatly loved that she had translated it into *langue d'oïl,* a dialect of medieval Northern France, much used by the troubadours. This was only one of many Breton lays which it gave her great delight to translate, and then to sing to her own harping, so that others, too, might enjoy them.

She tells us:

"Many a lay, on many a day, the minstrel has chanted to my delighted ear. I could not let them perish, forgotten, by the wayside. So in my turn I have made a new song of them, rhymed as well as I am able. Writing them has often kept me sleepless in my bed all through the night."

She herself found the Breton lays so enchanting that she would always begin her singing of one of them with an introduction such as this:

"Now I will sing before you a very ancient Breton lay, even as it was sung to me. For this lay is sweet to hear, and the tune lovely to remember."

And she would end the lay with praise such as this:

"Fair is this tale and sweet this tune that minstrels chant to harp and viol. Such lays may be heard in Brittany and in many another realm beside. I, also, who have sung it and set it down in writing, have been happy just in telling over this fair tale. Long may the remembrance of such tales endure!"

THE LAY OF SIR LANVAL

THE LAY OF SIR LANVAL

I.   HOW THE MAIDEN SENT FOR SIR LANVAL

Marie de France sings:

Listen, lordlings, to the words of Marie. Let the folk about the fire be silent when the minstrel tunes her harp and tells her tale. Now will I sing before you a very ancient Breton Lay. With a glad heart will I sing this lay, which once I heard a Breton minstrel chanting to his harp, and which the scribe has written down for our delight.

 IR LANVAL was the poorest of King Arthur's knights. He could afford to lodge in only the humblest hostel. He could give no lordly gifts. He and his squire, his page and his groom, went clad most simply. Because of his poverty he never sought, with the other knights, the company of Queen Guinevere's ladies.

But by his companions Sir Lanval was greatly beloved, for he was a most courteous knight, and as brave as he was courteous. Especially was he dear to those two brave and courteous cousins, Sir Gawain and Sir Owain.

One fair spring day, Sir Lanval rode out from King Arthur's Court alone, to take pleasure in the sights and sounds of the countryside. Riding through the green meadows, he came to a river of clear, running water; and this he would have crossed, although there was no ford, but his horse hung back, trembling.

So Sir Lanval dismounted, and, turning his horse loose to crop the fresh grass, he laid himself down on the river bank, with his folded cloak for a pillow. And here he lay, thinking now of his poverty, and now of the sunlight and the breaking leaf-buds and the song of the birds in the boughs above him.

Presently, turning his head, Sir Lanval saw two damsels coming towards him over the green grass. Both were most beautiful and delicate of face and form, and they wore the richest of kirtles and mantles. He rose to his feet, and bowed, and greeted them with respect and courtesy.

"Sir Lanval," said the elder, "the lady whom we serve prays you to follow us, for she would speak with you."

"Our lady is very near at hand," added the younger. "Look yonder! There her tent is spread."

Sir Lanval looked, and saw that a pavilion was pitched nearby, in a fair place in the meadow. It was of rich silk woven in many bright colours. The lances that upheld it were of gold; its cords and fringes were of golden thread; and above it was set an eagle made all of gold, glittering in the sun as if it were in flight.

"I am at your lady's service," said Sir Lanval, bowing. "Right glad shall I be to do your lady's bidding."

And, leaving his horse still quietly grazing, he was led by the two damsels to the pavilion.

"Our lady is called The Maiden," they told him, as they stood aside for him to enter.

Within the pavilion The Maiden awaited him, whiter than any altar-lily, more beautiful than any damsel he had ever beheld. No castle's spoil could furnish a richer coverlet than that on the couch on which she reclined. She was clad in a fair kirtle of spotless white linen, and over it a costly ermine mantle, edged with purple. Sir Lanval stood still as a stone in the pavilion doorway, gazing entranced upon so sweet a sight.

The Maiden beckoned him to come nearer, and to seat himself at the foot of her couch. When he had done so, she said:

"Lanval, for your sake have I come from my distant country. I have seen how patiently you have borne your poverty, and I have loved you for it from afar. Now I bring and offer you this love."

Lanval replied, moved to deep joy:

"Fair lady, since it pleases you to be so gracious, I devote myself altogether to your service. There is nothing in the world I would not do for you."

"Dear friend," she said, "I lay only one charge upon you – that you speak to no-one of me and of our love. For then never in all your life on earth would you see my face again."

Sir Lanval gave his word that he would honour her command most strictly.

"But my prayer would be," he added, "that you would never send me from your side."

"That may not be as yet," she answered. "But as long as you do not speak of me to others, you may see me at your pleasure. You have only to think of me and I shall be beside you."

Then the two damsels who had led Lanval to the pavilion entered, one bearing a golden bowl filled with clear water, and the other a towel of soft white linen. When Sir Lanval had washed his hands, they clothed him in new rich garments, and he and The Maiden sat down at table and broke bread together.

When they had eaten, the two damsels brought Sir Lanval's horse, gay now in rich new trappings. As he mounted to ride back to King Arthur's Court, The Maiden's farewell words were these:

"Fair friend, from now on spend at will. For the more gold and silver you give to the needy, the more gold and silver will you find again in your pouch."

And so indeed it was. From then on, Sir Lanval spent largely, but always his purse was filled. To all who were in need of a lodging he gave hospitality in his hostel. To all who knew poverty as he had once known it, he gave lordly gifts. He redeemed the captive. He fed the poor. He clothed the minstrel in scarlet. And he had but to think of The Maiden, and there she was beside him!

Because of this, he loved still to be alone, as he had been on that day when he had been led to the pavilion in the meadow. So he still did not seek, as his fellow-knights did, the company of Queen Guinevere's ladies; for the company of this one lady was all he asked of life.

II.   HOW SIR LANVAL DISPLEASED QUEEN GUINEVERE

OW on Midsummer Day a band of King Arthur's knights went together into an orchard to enjoy each other's company out-of-doors in the warm June weather. Sir Gawain and Sir Owain were among them; and presently Sir Gawain said to his cousin:

"Why is our comrade Lanval not with us? Let us go and fetch him that we may enjoy this summer sun together."

So they went together to Sir Lanval's hostel, and persuaded him to return with them to the orchard.

Now this orchard was at the foot of the tower in which Queen Guinevere had her apartments. When she heard the laughter and gaiety of the knights below, she looked out of her window and saw them there and said to her ladies:

"Let us go down and join that happy company."

So she and her ladies made themselves beautiful and went down into the orchard.

When the knights saw the Queen and her ladies descending the steps from the tower, they were filled with delight, and each one hastened forward to greet his favourite lady, and to lead her by the hand along the winding paths beneath the apple trees, and to whisper merry compliments in her ear.

But Sir Lanval drew a little apart and stood alone; for there was only one lady he longed to be with, and that was his own Maiden.

When the Queen saw him go apart, she followed him, and, seating herself on the grass, she called him to come and sit near her.

"Lanval," she said, "I have long honoured you as a worthy knight. You have only one failing. Why do you so deeply despise all ladies and their love that there is not one among my damsels who is pleasant in your eyes?"

Then Lanval, anxious to soothe the Queen, replied hastily, forgetful of The Maiden's warning:

"Lady, all your damsels are most pleasant in my eyes. But The Maiden whom I love would bear the prize from every lady in the land."

Now Queen Guinevere was renowned as the most beautiful of ladies then living, so that Sir Lanval's tactless words affronted her. She rose to her feet and left the orchard and went up to her chamber in great displeasure. And when King Arthur returned that evening from hunting the deer and sought her in her chamber, she fell weeping at his feet; and when he asked her why she wept, she told him:

"Sire, your knight Sir Lanval has thrown it in my face that the lady of his love is more beautiful than I."

King Arthur came forth from the Queen's chamber and called to him three lords of his household.

"Go to Sir Lanval's hostel," he bade them, "and bring him to my presence."

The three lords went at once to Sir Lanval's hostel, and found him sitting there in deep sorrow, his head sunk in his hands. For the first time since his first meeting with The Maiden, when he had thought of her he had not found her at his side. In mounting despair he had implored her to come to him; but still she had not come. How bitterly now did he repent that hasty breaking of his promise never to speak of her to anyone in the outside world!

So bowed down was he with his great grief that he rose without a word and went with the three lords to King Arthur's presence in dejected silence.

"Lanval," said the King, "the Queen accuses you of boasting most uncourteously to her that your lady's beauty far exceeds her own."

Sir Lanval stood before the King, downcast and dumb.

"Lanval," said the King, "have you nothing to say on this matter?"

Sir Lanval aroused himself out of his heart-sickness to reply.

"Sire," he said, "I did indeed tell the Queen that The Maiden whom I love would bear the prize from every lady in the land; and already I have paid so dearly for these hasty words that if any man had slain me on my way to you I would have counted him my friend. But it would have been a foul deed to set such shame upon the Queen as she has read into my words, and of that at least I am not guilty."

Then King Arthur said to the three lords:

"Sirs, give me wise counsel in this matter, that wrong may be done to none. For I fear the Queen will need more than Lanval's assurance to appease her wrath."

Then said the oldest and wisest of the three lords:

"Sire, give us three leave to go aside and debate upon this matter."

King Arthur gave them leave, and the three lords went aside.

"I would show proper reverence to our own lord liege," said the eldest of the lords. "But by the faith that I owe this company, what has our comrade done amiss save brag of the beauty of his damsel, and so prick the Queen's pride?"

"If the lady's beauty is as great as Lanval says," said the second lord, "then his guilt lies only in his discourtesy in speaking plain truth to the Queen."

"Let Lanval send for his lady," suggested the third. "If her beauty is such as he has said, the Queen will have no cause for wrath, and she must pardon Lanval his hasty words, since it will be plain that he did not speak out of malice."

"And if she will not come, or if she comes and her beauty falls below Lanval's boast, then let him be cast out of our fellowship and sent forth from the service of the King," the oldest, wisest lord summed up.

As this counsel seemed good to them all, they returned and laid it before King Arthur, who also found it good, and bade Sir Lanval send for his lady.

"Sire," replied Sir Lanval, "I will pray her to come, but I fear her love is lost to me through my folly in speaking of her. If this is so, I shall care little what befalls me. I am content to submit myself to the judgment of your lords."

Then the lords of the household appointed a day on which judgment should be given, till when Sir Lanval's sword was taken from him, and Sir Gawain, Sir Owain and others of Sir Lanval's fellowship gladly gave into King Arthur's hand pledges that their comrade would present himself in the judgment hall on the appointed day.

So Sir Lanval returned to his hostel, and a great company of his friends went with him to keep him in good heart, and came every day to his chamber to cheer his heaviness. But Sir Lanval was not to be comforted; for though he thought day and night of The Maiden, she never once came to his side; and more grievous to him than any verdict of the judges was the knowledge that he had broken faith with The Maiden and so forfeited her love.

III. HOW THE MAIDEN CAME TO SIR LANVAL'S HELP

O N the day appointed, all the lords of the King's household came together to give judgment. King Arthur sat on his throne on the dais, with Queen Guinevere beside him. Sir Gawain and Sir Owain and those other comrades who had stood surety for Sir Lanval escorted him into the hall and grouped themselves about him. The rest of the hall was so full of knights and ladies that there was not room to cast a rose among them.

The babble of voices died away and silence fell on the crowded hall as the hour of noon drew near, for this was the hour at which judgment was to be given if Sir Lanval's lady had not yet appeared. King Arthur sent out to his gate-keeper to ask if any cavalcade were in sight, but the gate-keeper sent back word that the paths across the plain beyond the city were as empty as his hand.

So now some of the lords said that there was nothing for it but to give judgment against Sir Lanval, while others counselled showing pity and patience and waiting a little while longer. Then Sir Gawain, who had climbed to a high window, called out loudly:
"There come two damsels pricking across the plain!"

At this a great hubbub broke out in the hall, and Sir Owain, leaning to Sir Lanval, whispered:
"Comrade, I will warrant one of them is your lady!"

Sir Lanval's heart began to thud, but he answered with misgiving:
"It is more than I dare hope. For in boasting of her beauty I have forfeited her love."

Soon they could hear a clatter of hoofs in the courtyard, then into the hall came two maidens, riding on two white palfreys. Very sweet and dainty were these two maidens, and richly robed in crimson silk. Every man there, king or lord or knight or squire, looked willingly upon them, so fair were they to see.

Sir Gawain leaned down from his window to ask:
"Lanval, comrade, which one is your love?"

But Lanval, gazing at them both, first with hope, then with despair, shook his head and answered:
"Neither. My Maiden is more beautiful than either."

The crush of knights and ladies parted to make a lane, and along it rode the two maidens to the dais. Here they dismounted and knelt before the King.
"Sire," said the elder one, "we have ridden ahead with the tidings that our lady comes to speak with you."

The King greeted them gladly. Two squires came to lead away their palfreys, and two knights brought the maidens courteously to where they might be seated among the ladies of the Queen.

Then Sir Gawain called again from his high window:

"I see two more damsels riding towards the palace!"

Again came the clatter of hoofs in the courtyard, then into the hall again came two maidens riding on two white Spanish mules. Over their kirtles they wore fresh white mantles, embroidered with gold. Every eye in the hall dwelt on them with pleasure, so modest were they of bearing and so gracious of person.

Sir Lanval's comrades were filled with hope, saying to one another:

"Surely these fair damsels have come to help our friend!"

And Sir Gawain leaned down from his window towards Sir Lanval, begging joyfully:

"Tell us truly, for the love of God, is not one of these your love?"

But Sir Lanval, gazing at their beauty, shook his head and answered as before:

"My Maiden is more beautiful than either!"

Again the crush of knights and ladies parted to make a lane, and along it rode the two maidens to the dais. Here they, too, dismounted and knelt before the King.

"Sire," said the elder, "we have ridden before with the tidings that our lady, who would speak with you, is very near at hand."

The King greeted them gladly. Two squires led away their mules, and two knights courteously brought the maidens to sit beside their companions. Many of the lords and ladies, gazing at them with pleasure, whispered to one another:

"In beauty either of these damsels surely outshines our Queen!"

And now there arose a tumult in the town outside, sounds of rejoicing in the streets, and the noise of feet running swiftly forth from houses.

Sir Gawain, looking out from his high window, saw riding towards the palace the flower of all the ladies in the world. At a slow pace she rode, graciously and softly, through streets lined with great and small, young and old, all rejoicing in the sight of so much beauty.

Sir Gawain came down from the window to Sir Lanval's side, asking joyfully a third time:

"Comrade, truly this time is it not your love who comes? She is neither dark nor golden, short nor tall. She is only the most lovely thing in all the world!"

As she slowly entered the hall, her white palfrey bearing her as if she loved her burden, Sir Lanval lifted his head and looked at her; and the blood came rushing to his face as he replied:

"It is indeed my love. I am healed of my hurt just by looking on her face!"

The crush of knights and ladies parted to make a lane, and along it she rode to the dais. There she dismounted and stood before King Arthur. The whole Court rose, and the King himself stepped down from the dais to meet her.

"Sire," she said, "I love Sir Lanval, the knight who stands there in disgrace. His tongue, alas, was over-hasty when speaking with the Queen. But now let your lords look boldly on my face and deal justly in this matter."

King Arthur commanded that this should be done. She loosed the clasp of her mantle of royal purple and stood gracious and modest in a kirtle spotless as snow. Every eye that dwelt on her marvelled at a fairness beyond that of earthly woman. Every heart felt quiet and content at the sight of so much beauty.

Since Sir Lanval had clearly spoken truly and without malice, the lords gave him back his sword. With The Maiden he took his leave of King Arthur and Queen Guinevere and all the Court. Gawain, Owain and all the rest of his fellowship escorted him, with The Maiden and her four damsels, to the marble mounting-block in the courtyard, where their steeds awaited them.

Mounting the stone, The Maiden seated herself on her white steed, behind Sir Lanval; her maidens mounted theirs; and out through the city and across the plain they rode, the whole Court watching them, till they were no more seen.

Marie sings:

The Bretons say that The Maiden took Sir Lanval to an island, very dim and very fair, that is called Avalon, and that there they dwell together still. I myself can tell you no more of the matter. But of the adventures of Sir Lanval and his faery love the courteous Bretons made this Lay, deeming it a joyous tale that men should not forget.

CHRÉTIEN DE·
TROYES AND HIS
VERSE·
·ROMANCES

CHRÉTIEN DE TROYES AND HIS 12TH CENTURY FRENCH VERSE-ROMANCES

OUR next story, *The Knight of the Cart*, is by Chrétien de Troyes. He wrote it in the second half of the twelfth century for the Countess Marie of Champagne, daughter of King Louis VII of France. He wrote it as a long verse-romance, to be recited rather than sung, so that although he lived at the same time as Marie de France, he was one small step further away than she was from the original Arthurian minstrelsy.

When he wrote this romance, Chrétien belonged to the Countess Marie's court at Troyes. Some people think he must have been a herald there, as in all his Arthurian stories he delights in describing jousts and tournaments and the devices on the shields and banners of the knights taking part in them. You will see that he describes the tournament in this story with great gusto and with real first-hand knowledge.

Several of the great medieval trade routes of Europe met in Troyes, and every year two famous trade fairs were held there. To these fairs came not only many merchants from many lands, but also story-tellers, minstrels, jongleurs and other entertainers. These brought with them songs and stories from every country in which the name and fame of King Arthur were known.

Four of these long stories Chrétien re-told in verse, writing in a clear and delightful style in medieval Northern French flavoured with the dialect of Champagne.

Chrétien tells us that he got his stories "from the story-tellers and from a book." As printing had not yet been invented, the "book" must have been a manuscript. This manuscript has disappeared, and Chrétien's delightful version of *The Knight of the Cart* is the only one that has come down to us.

THE KNIGHT OF THE CART

THE KNIGHT OF THE CART

I. HOW QUEEN GUINEVERE WAS KIDNAPPED AND A KNIGHT RODE IN A CART

ONE Ascension Day, when King Arthur was holding Court at Camelot, an unknown knight strode arrogantly into the hall. "King Arthur!" he cried. "I hold captive many knights and ladies of this your land of Logres. I will release them on one condition."

"And what is that condition, Sir Knight?" King Arthur asked.

And the unknown knight replied:

"That you send Queen Guinevere, attended by one knight, after me into the forest. I will meet him there in single combat. If he wins, he shall bring her safely back to you and all my captives from Logres shall go free. If he loses, the Queen comes with me."

Then, without farewell, he turned and strode abruptly from the hall.

At this a great uproar arose among King Arthur's knights, and Sir Kay of the Wry Tongue sprang from his seat and cried out to the king:

"Sire, with your leave or without it, I withdraw from your service here and now."

"But why, Kay?" asked King Arthur in astonishment.

Sir Kay tossed his head.

"I would not stay a moment longer," he vowed, "for many measures of fine gold."

King Arthur turned to Queen Guinevere in dismay.

"My lady dear," he said, "beg Kay to stay with us."

"Kay," said the Queen, "we should never again be happy if we lost your company. There is nothing in the world we would not do to keep you with us."

"Lady," said Kay, "if you and the king will grant me a favour, I will remain."

"Kay," said the King and Queen together, "we grant it, whatever it is."

"It is this," said Kay, "that the Queen and I may follow into the forest the knight who has just left us."

At this the Queen turned pale and the King's face fell. But never yet in all his life had he failed to keep his word. So in silence he placed the Queen's hand in Kay's, and in silence all the court followed them from the hall into the courtyard. In silence many heads were shaken as the Queen and Kay mounted and rode away, for all were asking in their hearts:

"Will the Queen ever come back?"

At last Sir Gawain, who was King Arthur's nephew, broke the silence.

"Uncle," he said, "shall we not all ride after them to see how Kay fares in the combat?"

All the knights eagerly agreed. They sent their pages to bring their horses; and when all were mounted, away they rode together to the forest. But Gawain rode faster than the rest, and so drew well ahead.

Presently he came to a glade where the ground had been trampled by horses and was littered with splintered lances; and a little further on he glimpsed along a vista of trees a knight going slowly on foot, burdened by his armour; and, some distance ahead of the knight, a cart driven by a dwarf, who sat on the shafts with a long goad in his hands.

When Gawain overtook the knight, the knight himself was just overtaking the cart and was asking the dwarf:

"Tell me, has my lady Queen Guinevere passed this way?"

The dwarf answered sullenly:

"If you want news of the Queen, get up into my cart, and tomorrow you will hear it."

Now it was a most shameful thing for a knight to be seen in a cart, for in those days criminals were placed in carts and paraded through the streets on their way to punishment or execution. So for one step, for two steps, the knight hesitated; then, making up his mind, he climbed up into the cart, which the dwarf drove on at a faster pace without another word.

Gawain rode quickly after them, calling to the dwarf:

"What *is* the news of the Queen?"

The dwarf replied with pursed lips:

"Get into the cart with this other knight, and you will hear it when *he* does."

"Having my steed, I would not wish to cumber your cart," said Gawain courteously. "I will be content to follow you."

So thus they went on through the forest, the unknown knight in the cart with the dwarf, and Gawain on his steed close behind.

II. HOW TWO KNIGHTS SAW THE KIDNAPPED QUEEN

T sunset they came to a town; and as soon as they entered its gate the people came running to mock and jeer at the knight riding in the cart.

"What is his crime?" they shouted to the dwarf. "And what is his punishment? Is he to be flayed? Or whipped? Or hanged? Or drowned? Or burnt?"

But without a word the dwarf drove on through the crowd into the courtyard of a tall tower, with Gawain riding close behind; and a damsel came out to welcome them into the hall. She, too, asked the dwarf what ill deed the knight riding in the cart had done; again he gave no answer, but signed to the knight to descend from the cart; then he silently drove it away.

The damsel brought the two knights into the hall, where her servants unarmed them and robed them in green mantles; and after supper two high, fine beds were set up in the hall, and in these the two guests slept till morning.

As they stood together next morning at a window overlooking the meadow below, they saw a litter being borne along the river bank, and behind the litter a tall knight on horseback leading a lady by her horse's rein.

Gawain turned to the Knight of the Cart and cried:

"That was Sir Kay on the litter!"

And the Knight of the Cart turned to Gawain and cried:

"That was Queen Guinevere riding behind it!"

Then quickly they armed, and Gawain sent word to the stables for his horse to be saddled immediately. The Damsel of the Tower came to escort them from the hall, and in the courtyard she gave the Knight of the Cart a parting gift of a fine steed and a new lance. And when they had taken courteous leave of her the two knights galloped like the wind along the river bank; but nowhere could they find any trace of the knight on the litter or of the tall knight leading the lady on her steed.

At last they reached a cross-roads, and reined in their horses, not knowing which of the other three tracks to follow. Then they saw a damsel approaching, and Gawain hailed her:

"Damsel, has a wounded knight on a litter passed this way?"

And the Knight of the Cart added:

"And a tall knight leading a lady on her steed?"

The damsel answered:

"Sirs, they have. Prince Meleagant has carried them captive to his father's castle in the Land of No Return.

Both knights asked together:

"Which of these roads leads to that castle?"

"These two both do," the damsel told them, "but both are perilous. For on this one you must cross a bridge under water, and on that one you must cross a bridge made of a sword."

Then the Knight of the Cart said to Gawain:

"Sir, let us each take a different bridge. Which one do you prefer?"

And Gawain replied:

"Sir, unless the bridge under water is your own choice, I will take that."

"Then I will gladly take the Sword-bridge," said the Knight of the Cart. "And whichever of us reaches the castle first, let him go to the other's bridge and meet him there."

To this Gawain gladly agreed. Then, after courteously taking leave of the damsel and of each other, each knight rode on, along the track of his choice.

III. HOW THE KNIGHT OF THE CART FOUND THE QUEEN'S COMB AND LIFTED THE LID OF HIS OWN TOMB

HE Knight of the Cart came presently to a ford, and on the other side was the knight who guarded it, with a damsel beside him.

"Knight," called the Knight of the Ford, "I am guarding this ford and forbid you to cross."

But the Knight of the Cart, unheeding, rode on into the water.

"By the heart in my breast," cried the Knight of the Ford, "as you come up out of the water I swear I will smite off your head!"

And he struck the Knight of the Cart so shrewd a blow that his lance splintered.

But in the fight that followed, the Knight of the Cart soon had the Knight of the Ford at his mercy, and would have slain him. But the damsel, wringing her hands, called out:

"Sir Knight, for my sake be merciful!"

Then the Knight of the Cart spared the other's life for the damsel's sake, and took leave of them both, and went on his way.

As night began to fall he overtook another damsel riding the same way. She said to him:

"Sir, my dwelling is near at hand. Shelter there this night."

And gladly the Knight of the Cart did so.

When the next day dawned, the damsel said she would accompany him a little on his road; so they set out together, riding side by side. Presently they came to a spring, and on its stone basin lay a comb of gilded ivory, shining as though it were the sun.

"Never," exclaimed the knight, "have I seen a comb so beautiful!"

"Never, indeed," agreed the damsel. "It must surely be the Queen's!"

"There are many queens," remarked the knight. "Have you a special one in mind?"

"Who but Queen Guinevere?" replied the damsel.

At that the knight leaned down from his saddle and picked up the comb; and as he gazed at it and at the bright hair clinging to its teeth, it seemed to him that gold refined a hundred thousand times would be less bright.

"Now I know that I chose the better road," he rejoiced. "For Queen Guinevere has surely only lately passed this way!"

So they rode on, and came to a forest, and beyond the forest to mown fields, and among the fields a church.

The knight dismounted and entered the church to pray, while the damsel held his horse for him. As he returned, he paused to look at the magnificent tombs around the church, and found carved on them the names of many famous knights who were still living. But the largest and most magnificent of all had no name carved on it.

While he stood marvelling, an ancient monk came towards him, and the knight asked him about this tomb.

The monk replied:

"Sir, it is recorded that he who can lift the stone lid of this tomb will free all the captives in this Land of No Return. But he would need to be a man as strong as seven."

Then the Knight of the Cart grasped the stone lid of the tomb and heaved. It opened so easily that the monk cried out in awe:

"Sir, tell me who you are!"

"I am a knight of Logres, the kingdom of King Arthur," said the Knight of the Cart. "Now pray tell *me*, for your part, who is to lie in this tomb?"

"Sir," said the monk, "he who can lift its lid."

So together they came to the damsel; and while the knight was mounting his steed, the old monk told her how he had lifted the lid of the tomb and asked her:

"Damsel, what is his name? For clearly this is his tomb."

"His name I do not know," she replied. "But one sure thing I can say — there is not such another alive where the four winds of heaven blow."

And there the three parted. The old monk remained, lost in thought; the damsel returned to her dwelling; and the Knight of the Cart rode on his way alone.

IV. HOW THE KNIGHT OF THE CART PASSED THE STONY PASSAGE AND HELPED THE CAPTIVES FROM LOGRES

S the evening drew on, the Knight of the Cart overtook a huntsman riding home from the chase.

"Sir," said the huntsman, "night will soon be upon us. Spend it with myself and my family."

The Knight gladly accepted; and when they reached the dwelling, he found himself made welcome by his host's wife and five sons. When he had been unarmed and clad in a fur mantle and they had all eaten together, his host asked him from which part of the land he came.

"I have but just come to this country from the Kingdom of Logres," the knight replied.

Then his host cried, sorely distressed:

"Alas, Sir Knight! We, too, are from Logres, and like all our countrymen we are held captive in this land. Whoever wishes may come into it; but once here, here he must stay."

"Sir," replied the knight, "when I have accomplished the task I came to do, I shall return to Logres, I promise you, and so shall you and all captives."

At this his host asked eagerly:

"Sir, are you the knight of whom we captives have heard rumours? Are you the knight who has come in search of our kidnapped Queen?"

"I am he," the knight assented. "Give me what counsel you can as to the way to the sword-bridge."

"I will give you better than counsel," said his host. "My two eldest sons shall guide you there."

So it was arranged, and they parted for the night.

Next morning, as soon as it was light, the Knight of the Cart set out with his two companions.

"Sir," they said to him, "we come first to the Stony Passage, which is so narrow that only one horse can go through it at a time. Through that we must fight our way."

Soon they saw a tall wooden tower in the distance, and the two youths told him:

"Sir, that is the tower that guards the Stony Passage. A watchman stands on it and warns the knight who guards the passage when strangers approach. Listen! You can hear his horn now!"

The Knight of the Cart heard the sound of the horn; and, as they drew nearer, he saw a knight ride forth from a gate at the foot of the tower, armed to the teeth and followed by servants brandishing sharp axes.

This knight stood barring the entrance to the Stony Passage, and shouted abuse as the Knight of the Cart drew nearer;

"Base churl, to have ridden in a cart! And fool to have entered this country!"

He rode swiftly towards the Knight of the Cart, engaging him in combat, while his servants attacked the huntsman's two sons with their axes. But soon the Knight of the Cart smote the Knight of the Stony Passage a blow that laid him flat on the stones, and at this the servants flung down their axes and cowered back, so that the Knight of the Cart and his two companions were able to ride through the passage unharmed.

Their path now led them across a plain towards a castle on a distant hill-top; and as they rode towards it they overtook a knight riding in the same direction, and all journeyed on together. Presently a squire came galloping in great haste towards them, crying out to their new companion:

"Master, make haste! The captives from Logres have rebelled and are attacking us! They say their deliverer is at hand!"

Then the squire and his master galloped like the wind to the castle, and the Knight of the Cart and the huntsman's two sons galloped with them. They all crossed the castle moat, and the portcullis fell behind them with a clang. They followed the squire across the castle courtyard and out through a postern gate. Below them they saw a great meadow in which a fierce battle was raging.

"Sir," said the elder of the huntsman's two sons, "I will go and discover which are our own people."

He rode down to the meadow and returned at once with the news:

"Sir, these are our people on this side of the field."

Then the Knight of the Cart rode straight into the fight, his two companions close behind him; and wherever they went there was a breaking of lances and a crushing of shields; and the joyful rumour travelled swiftly among the captives from Logres: "He who is to deliver us is here!"

With this news their courage revived and their strength with it; and so many brave deeds were done that when dusk fell and ended the fighting, this first battle of the rebellion had been won.

And after a joyful night spent among the captives from Logres, at dawn next day the Knight of the Cart and his two companions continued their journey towards the sword-bridge.

V.   HOW THE KNIGHT OF THE CART FOUGHT THE KNIGHT OF THE SWORD-BRIDGE

LL that day the Knight of the Cart and his two companions rode on without any adventure, till, just as the sun was setting, they came out of a forest and saw before them a dwelling, and at its open door a gentle lady was sitting.

When she saw them she rose and welcomed them and begged them to honour her house that night, then called her three sons to lead away their horses and curry them well, and her three daughters to remove their armour and replace it with soft mantles.

No sooner had they done this than the master of the house returned from his work as a forester, and his daughters ran to meet him with the news:

"Father! Father! We have three guests this evening!"

"God be praised for that!" he said.

And he came in and welcomed his guests, and they all sat down to supper.

Scarcely had they eaten their first mouthful when the door flew open, and in came a knight on a charger, armed from head to foot, looking as proud as a bull — and a bull is a very proud beast. He rode towards them with a challenging air, demanding:

"Which of you is the fool who intends to cross the sword-bridge?"

The Knight of the Cart replied with dignity:

"I am he who intends to cross the sword-bridge."

"You?" sneered the other. "Have you forgotten the cart? Do you feel no shame for your ride in it? If you cross the water, it will be in my boat, and on the far bank I shall take your head as toll! Otherwise you must come outside, here and now, and meet me hand to hand in single combat."

"If that is the custom of the Sword-bridge, " said the Knight of the Cart, "I will obey it."

He rose from the table; his armour and horse were brought; and they met on a stretch of level ground beyond the gate. Everyone in the house came out to watch the encounter.

The two knights dealt each other hard blows; and when both were unhorsed they attacked each other on foot. Neither had the advantage till the Knight of the Cart called up all his strength and rushed at his adversary like a storm-wind, dubbing him so soundly that not a string nor strap remained unbroken, so that his helmet fell from his head and he cried aloud for mercy.

"Then you must mount on a cart," said the Knight of the Cart.

"I would rather die than mount on a cart," cried the Knight of the Sword-bridge.

"Then die you must," said the Knight of the Cart.

"I beg and beseech you," cried the Knight of the Sword-bridge, "do not compel me to mount on a cart!"

Across the meadow came a maiden, riding a tawny mule as fast as it would go.

"Knight," she called, "I come to ask a favour."

"Damsel," said the Knight of the Cart, "if it is in my power to grant it, it is already yours."

"It is the head of this vanquished knight," she told him. "For he is the basest creature that ever was or ever shall be. And this I know, that if you spare him today, he will not spare you tomorrow."

The Knight of the Cart pondered. He had never yet refused his mercy to any fallen foe who had sued for it; yet the damsel had his promise.

"Knight of the Sword-bridge," he said. "I will give you time to re-arm, and we will fight this fight again. But if this time I should win, there can be no mercy."

The fallen knight rose eagerly, sure that this time he would win; and as for showing mercy himself, that had never been his custom. So again they fought; and again the Knight of the Cart proved victor. This time he did not hesitate, but kept his promise to the damsel.

As she rode away into the twilight with her grisly gift, she called back to him:

"Sir Knight, you have done well to grant my boon. At the appointed time you shall receive a reward beyond your imagining."

As they all returned to the house, his host said to the Knight of the Cart:

"Sir, your two companions have told me that you are that valiant knight from Logres who turned the tide of battle yesterday. My family and I are captives from Logres, and everything we have is at your service."

The Knight of the Cart thanked him, and next morning he and his two companions said farewell and set out, well furnished with fresh horses and armour.

And late that same afternoon they reached the sword-bridge.

VI.   HOW THE KNIGHT OF THE CART CROSSED THE SWORD-BRIDGE

HEN they reached the sword-bridge, the Knight of the Cart and his two companions dismounted and looked about them. And this was what they saw:

A stream raging across their path, cold, black, swift, and whirling, and looking as bottomless as the salt sea.

A bridge spanning this stream, made of a polished, gleaming sword as long as two lances.

On each bank of the stream a tree into whose trunk one end of the sword was driven.

And at the far end of the bridge a great rock to which two lions were chained.

As they looked at all this, the knight's two companions began to tremble with fear.

"Fair sir," the elder cried, "you *cannot* cross this raging torrent on a sword-edge!"

"And should you fall," cried his brother, "this devil's stream would swallow you in an instant!"

"And if, with heaven's help, you *did* cross," went on the first, "those two fierce lions are waiting to tear you to pieces!"

"To suck the blood from your veins!" added the second.

"To eat your flesh!" moaned the first.

"And then to gnaw your bones!" groaned the second.

But the Knight of the Cart only laughed as he answered:

"Sirs, your concern comes from your kind hearts. Receive my thanks for it. But I fear the bridge and the stream no more than I fear this dry land. I would rather die than turn back now!"

Then, dismounting, he removed the armour from his hands and feet.

"Sir, why do you do that?" asked the elder brother.

And the Knight of the Cart explained:

"So that I may cling the better to the sword-edge."

"But that is sharper than a scythe" cried the younger brother. "And you have kept on your feet neither sole nor upper nor hose."

"Better to maim myself," said the Knight of the Cart, "than to fall into this torrent and be swept away."

"Alas!" wailed the elder brother. "In how sorry a state will you reach the other side!"

But the Knight of the Cart laughed again, then embraced them and bade them farewell, thanking them for their company, and sending back in their care the horse their father had lent him, with many courteous messages to all their family.

Then, while they stood and watched him with bated breath, he began to creep on hands and knees across the sword-bridge.

He found that all that they had said was only too true. The sword's edge was indeed even sharper than a scythe. But so confused were his senses by the black, boiling water below that he was glad to cling to that sharpness.

Creeping inch by inch on wounded hands and knees and feet, he passed slowly above the roaring whirlpools in long-drawn-out agony. He did not dare to pause to consider how he was to confront the two lions when (and if) he reached the other side.

But when he did reach the other side, and lifted his sweatbeaded brow and looked about him, he could see no lions. He could not even see so much as a lizard on the bank.

Dragging himself wearily but thankfully on to the sweet grass beneath the tree-trunk which held fast the sword-tip, he raised his right hand and stared into the stone in the ring he wore on his first finger. This ring was a gift from the Lady of the Lake, who had brought him up from his infancy. By gazing into its stone he could tell whether he had been deceived by enchantment.

There were no lions visible in the stone. He knew then that they had been a magical illusion.

Joyful cries rang out from the other bank when the two brothers saw him safely cross. Blood from his wounds reddened the grass on which he lay. But, as he lay, he too gave thanks for his safe crossing.

He lay with closed eyes till his ebbing strength returned. Then he opened them and lifted himself, leaning on an elbow while he scanned the countryside spread out before him.

The green meadow in which he lay ran uphill to the horizon, where a great castle stood, and at the end of it a tower. Never had he seen a tower more kingly.

And as he gazed at it, his heart beat fast, for it seemed to him that it was in such a tower that he would find Queen Guinevere.

VII. HOW KING BADEMAGU BEFRIENDED THE KNIGHT OF THE CART

AT a window in this tower sat King Bademagu, the king of that country, a king good, wise, courteous and kind. At his side stood his son, Prince Meleagant, tall, handsome, strong, formidable in battle, but with a heart without gentleness or pity.

From their window both had seen the Knight of the Cart's agonised crossing of the sword-bridge. When the king saw him reach the nearer bank, he rejoiced with him in his achievement. But the prince's colour changed with the rage and spite which swept him.

"Son," said Bademagu, "we have just witnessed one of the boldest deeds that ever entered the mind of man. You must surely be as well-disposed as I am towards this heroic knight. You must show him honour, and give him freely and courteously what he has come in search of."

But Prince Meleagant answered angrily:

"Never, never will I surrender Queen Guinevere to him so tamely! If he comes for her, he must challenge me for her, and win her from me by force of arms."

"My son," said the king quietly, "evil will come of it if you do not heed my advice."

But Prince Meleagant retorted:

"Why should I give up to him that which I most wish to keep?"

King Bademagu rose from his seat at the window.

"I will say nothing more now," he said, "but will go to help this knight, for I am altogether on his side."

The king went down from the tower, and called for his horse and a horse-litter. Then, with a few of his attendants, he rode down the hill to the sword-bridge. There he found the Knight of the Cart staunching his wounds and wiping the blood from them. He might as well have expected to staunch the sea.

The king dismounted and came towards the knight, who at once rose to greet him as if he were hale and sound.

"Sir," said King Bademagu, "I am king of this land. I come to welcome you to it and to offer you my service. You come, I am sure, in search of Queen Guinevere?"

"That is so, Sire," the Knight of the Cart replied.

"I fear you must suffer hardship to obtain her," said the king. "But first your wounds must be cared for and completely healed."

"The Queen is safe and well, Sire?" asked the knight.

"The Queen is well, and safe in my own keeping," the king assured him. "Unless my son defeats you in single combat, there she will remain till you are ready to escort her back to Logres."

"Sire," said the knight, "I thank you. My wounds do not pain me, so let us lose no time. Let me meet your son in single combat tomorrow."

"I do not advise this so soon, but all shall be done as you wish," the king replied courteously.

Then the King's attendants lifted the knight and placed him in the horse-litter, from which he made gestures of farewell to his two young companions on the far bank of the stream. They, in turn, made signs of thankfulness that he had fallen into good hands, and when they had watched the cavalcade climb the hill to the castle, they joyfully mounted their horses and rode homewards.

Meanwhile, King Bademagu brought the wounded knight into the tower, and had a comfortable lodging-place prepared for him there, and sent to him a surgeon, who dressed his wounds with skill and care.

This done, the king went in search of his son.

"Son," he said when he had found him, "the knight is sorely wounded and stands in great need of rest. But it is his wish to do battle with you tomorrow."

"If *he* is anxious for the battle," said Prince Meleagant, "so am I, a hundred times more than he. And may no greater hardship ever visit me than that!"

So it was arranged; and the king, leaving his son, sent a good strong horse and handsome armour to the wounded knight, in readiness for the combat.

Meanwhile the news spread throughout the countryside. All that night the churches were filled with captive maidens from King Arthur's realm who had gone there fasting and walking barefoot in their shifts to pray for victory for the knight from Logres. And from dusk to dawn knights and ladies, barons and damsels, had come travelling to the castle from far and wide, so that when morning came there was such a press in the courtyard before the tower that there was not room to move one's foot.

For it was in this courtyard that Prince Meleagant and the Knight of the Cart were to meet in single combat.

VIII. HOW THE KNIGHT OF THE CART FOUGHT PRINCE MELEAGANT

AS soon as it was light, Prince Meleagant and the Knight of the Cart, both fully armed, were led mounted into the courtyard. King Bademagu came to them there, trying still, even at the last moment, to settle the matter peacefully; but Prince Meleagant spurned his father's efforts with scorn.

Then the king said, sighing:

"Rein in your horses till I reach my tower-window. Grant me at least that."

For the previous evening Queen Guinevere had begged him to place her where she would have a clear view of the combat. So now he went to bring her to the tower-window with the best view of the courtyard. He took his own place at a second window, and close behind them both pressed many knights and dames and damsels. As soon as the heralds saw the king seated at his window, they raised their trumpets and blew; and the combat began.

Prince Meleagant and the Knight of the Cart spurred at each other so violently that their steeds met head on, clashing breast to breast. Their lances split and splintered; their shields crashed like thunder-claps; burning sparks from their helmets flew in the air. They rushed at each other like two wild boars; blood spurted from helmet and harness.

Presently the wounds made when the Knight of the Cart crossed the sword-bridge began to cause his hands to weaken, and a murmur passed round the throng that Prince Meleagant would be victor.

Now among those watching at Queen Guinevere's window was a wise damsel who said to herself:

"If only the Queen's knight knew that the Queen was watching, it would give him new strength. If only I knew his name I would call and let him know."

So she pressed close to the Queen and asked:

"Lady, what is the name of your knight?"

And the Queen replied:

"His name is Lancelot du Lake."

Then the damsel leaned out of the window and called clearly:

"Lancelot, look round and see who is watching you!"

The Knight of the Cart turned and saw Queen Guinevere seated at the tower-window; and his strength came flooding back. He went on gazing up at her, fighting with backward blows, till the damsel called again:

"Lancelot, turn, so that you face the Queen!"

Then Lancelot, filled with new joy, and courage, rushed upon Prince Meleagant, compelling him to turn, pressing him rapidly towards the tower, driving him to and fro, always stopping before the Queen, so that soon the King began to feel sorry for his son.

He rose and went to Queen Guinevere and said:

"Lady, I plainly see that my son is getting the worst of this battle. I would not wish to see him slain."

"Fair Sire," the Queen replied, "you have treated me with such courtesy that to please you I would have my defender cease to fight your son."

She said this so clearly that both Lancelot and Prince Meleagant heard. Lancelot at once stood still and did not raise a hand, while the Prince, beside himself with rage and shame, continued to strike at him furiously with all the strength at his command, so that the King went down from the tower and into the lists, and bade his barons hold his son, and sadly said to him:

"So help me God, now there is nothing left but for you to give up the Queen."

So the combat ended; and the terms of the peace were these:

Prince Meleagant was to surrender the Queen into Lancelot's safe-keeping, and Lancelot was to escort her back to King Arthur's court in Logres. There, within a year of whenever Prince Meleagant demanded it, Lancelot was to fight him again; if Lancelot failed to obey the prince's summons, the Queen was to return with the prince to this, his father's country, and no-one was to hinder this or interfere.

As Lancelot and Prince Meleagant retired from the lists to remove their armour and have salves applied to their hurts, the crowds in the courtyard called down blessings on Lancelot and pressed forward to touch him, and the captives from Logres rejoiced, saying:

"Now shall we all be free!"

And when Lancelot had bathed and had put on a soft robe and mantle, he begged the King to take him to the Queen; and the King took him by the hand and led him to the hall in which the Queen awaited him.

IX. HOW QUEEN GUINEVERE SCORNED THE KNIGHT OF THE CART

WHEN King Bademagu entered the hall, holding Lancelot by the hand, Queen Guinevere rose and curtseyed to the King but looked at Lancelot coldly and spoke no word to him.

"Lady," said the King courteously, "here I bring you Lancelot. You must be greatly pleased to see him."

"I, Sire?" replied the Queen. "To see him gives me no pleasure at all."

"No pleasure," exclaimed the astonished King, "to see one who has exposed his life to mortal danger for your sake, and rescued you from my son who had so deeply wronged you?"

"Sire," said the Queen, "he has made but poor use of his time."

Lancelot, dumbfounded, said humbly:

"Lady, I am grieved at this."

But the Queen did not deign to answer a single word. Bowing to the King, she turned and swept out of the hall.

The King said to Lancelot, full of sympathy:

"Alas, Lancelot! What misdeed have you done to make the Queen like this?"

"Sire," replied Lancelot in distress, "I do not know; but whatever it is, she is in the right."

"No, Lancelot," said the King firmly. "Whatever it is, she is in the wrong; for again and again you have risked your life for her. Come away now, fair friend, and visit Sir Kay, who is not yet healed of his wounds."

The King led Lancelot to the room in which Sir Kay lay, recovering from the wounds received in his encounter with Prince Meleagant in the forest outside Camelot. There the King left the two knights together.

"How fares it with you, Kay?" asked Lancelot.

"Badly," Kay replied. "I would have died but for the old king's kindness. But each time he has sent a surgeon to apply a good plaster to my wounds, his son has sent another to take it off and apply a harmful one. So they heal but slowly."

"I hear," said Lancelot, "that the King is also kindness itself to our Queen."

"That is so," agreed Kay. "But is it true, as I hear, that she is *not* kindness itself to you?"

"It is true," confessed Lancelot. "For God's sake, can you tell me how I have displeased her?"

"I do not know," confessed Kay, "and I am greatly surprised at it."

"Well," sighed Lancelot, "I must leave it then unsolved; for now I must take my leave and seek Gawain at the water-bridge. For we arranged that whichever one of us first entered the land should go to meet the other."

After taking leave of the King, Lancelot went out into the courtyard, which was filled with the rejoicing captives from Logres whom his victory over Prince Meleagant had set free. They flocked and pressed about him.

"Sir," they asked, "what are we to do now?"

"What are the Queen's wishes?" Sir Lancelot asked.

And they told him:

"Her own knights and ladies she keeps with her still, on our lord Gawain's account, for his arrival is expected at any hour, and she says she will not leave for Logres till she sees him safe and sound."

Then Lancelot directed them:

"All those who also wish to stay with the Queen till she goes home should do so. And all those who wish to return at once to Logres should do so. And all those who wish to go to meet my lord Gawain may come with me to do so."

Then many joyfully shouted that they would go to meet Sir Gawain. So, sad that he must leave without a friendly farewell from the Queen, Lancelot set out with them on the way to the water-bridge.

X. HOW QUEEN GUINEVERE FORGAVE THE KNIGHT OF THE CART

QUICKLY the news spread that the captive Queen of Logres, and all the other captives from Logres, were planning to leave the country. This enraged the simple country-folk; and when they heard that Lancelot had obtained the victory over Prince Meleagant, they said to one another:

"Our King must be very angry. He will be pleased with us if we seize this Knight of the Cart and bring him back to him a prisoner."

So, armed from top to toe, a great band of them hid in a narrow ravine through which Lancelot had to pass on his way to the water-bridge.

Now, trusting in the peace and friendship between King Bademagu and themselves, Lancelot and all who were with him were travelling quite unarmed. So it was not difficult for the armed mob to seize Lancelot and make him their prisoner, lashing his feet together beneath his horse.

Those who were with him said to Lancelot's captors:

"Sirs, you cannot do this. Your King has given us his safe conduct, and we are under his protection."

"We know nothing of that," their captors replied. "You are our prisoners and we are taking you to our King."

And, guarding their prisoners well, they set out for King Bademagu's castle.

But a rumour reached the King more quickly than they did — a rumour that some of his subjects had seized Lancelot and put him to death.

The King, sorely grieved, swore:

"Those who have done this deed shall die themselves for it."

The rumour reached Queen Guinevere when she was sitting at meat; the shock of it almost killed her as she sat.

She mourned within herself:

"He came to this country for my sake, and I scorned him. Ah, if only he were still alive, how fully I would make amends!"

But when Lancelot and his captors were five or six leagues away from the castle, the glad news reached King Bademagu that the knight was still alive. He went at once to tell Queen Guinevere.

"Fair Sire, I thank you with all my heart," she said. "I would never have known happiness again if such a knight had been slain in my service."

When Lancelot arrived at the castle, safe and sound, (but with his feet still lashed together beneath his horse), there was great rejoicing. King Bademagu would have had his captors put to death there and then; but Lancelot interceded for them, and made peace between the King and his subjects.

Then the King took Lancelot again to see Queen Guinevere; and this time there was no warmth wanting in her welcome, so that Lancelot was encouraged to enquire:

"Lady, why had you no word for me when last we met?"

"Can you not think of a reason?" she asked, smiling.

"Was it because I had ridden in a cart on my search for you?" he suggested.

And she replied, smiling again:

"No. Rather it was because you had hesitated to do so for two whole steps!"

"Lady, you are quite right!" exclaimed Lancelot. "Receive my amends. And tell me if you can ever pardon me?"

"You are pardoned already," smiled the Queen.

So the rift between them was healed; and they and all their friends were joyful.

XI. HOW A DWARF DECOYED THE KNIGHT OF THE CART

PRESENTLY Lancelot, anxious to keep his pact with Gawain, asked leave of King Bademagu and Queen Guinevere to depart, and set out again with his company of freed captives from Logres.

They were approaching a crossroads within a league of the water-bridge when a dwarf with a scourge in his hand came galloping to meet them on a mighty hunter.

"Which of you is my lord Lancelot?" he asked.

Lancelot replied:

"I am he."

"My lord," said the dwarf, "my message is that you are to come with me swiftly to a goodly place nearby. Let your people wait here meanwhile, for you shall soon return to them."

So Lancelot bade his men rest awhile till his return, and himself followed the dwarf.

Time passed, but neither Lancelot nor the dwarf returned. Lancelot's companions sought high and low, but they could find no trace of either.

"Alas!" they said to each other. "That dwarf has decoyed our leader and betrayed him."

So, when they had waited some time further and sought high and low for Lancelot all over again, they took counsel together and decided to divide into two bands, one band to go forward to the water-bridge, and the other band to stay behind in case Lancelot should return. And if he had not done so by the time Gawain arrived, then they would search for Lancelot again under Gawain's direction.

So, with heavy hearts, the two bands parted.

When the first band reached the water-bridge, they found it was a bridge under water, with the same amount of water above it as below. It was only a foot and a half both in width and in thickness. And over it and under it the swift stream rushed turbulently.

The bridge was empty; but on the further bank they could see a riderless horse standing, and beside him a lance and a shield leaning against a tree. They shouted till the echoes rang; but no other voice replied.

Then they moved downstream, their searching glances raking both banks as well as the water between. And presently in the latter they glimpsed a body in armour, tossed to and fro by the current. One moment it rose, the next it sank; one moment they saw it, the next it was no longer to be seen.

Everything now that could help them they pressed into service – reins, lances, branches, shields; and after many efforts they at last succeeded in bringing the body to land.

"He is dead," said one.

"Could one expect him to be alive?" said another.

"He is full of water," said a third. "How can we tell whether he lives until we rid him of it?"

So they removed his helmet from his head, and his hauberk from his back, and his greaves from his legs, and upended him and let the river run out of him. Then those who understood these things knelt beside him and worked on his body.

"Now the passage-way to his heart is free," they reported. "Now I can feel his blood-beat. Look, he breathes! Soon he will speak."

And soon indeed he opened his eyes and looked around him and in a faint voice thanked them for rescuing him from the river. He told them that he was Gawain, a knight of Logres; and they told him that they also were of Logres, and gave him news of Queen Guinevere and of how Lancelot had been decoyed on his way to meet him.

At that he rose and came with them in haste to where their companions awaited them. These reported that they had again scoured the countryside but again had found no trace of Lancelot.

Then Gawain said:

"Then this is my counsel: that we go as speedily as possible to King Bademagu and place this whole matter in his hands, for his power and his resources in this land far exceed our own."

And to this they all agreed with one accord.

XII. HOW QUEEN GUINEVERE RETURNED TO KING ARTHUR'S COURT

WHEN Gawain and his company reached the castle, King Bademagu's joy over Gawain's coming was equalled only by his anxiety over Lancelot's disappearance; and without delay he sent out band after band of trusted men to search up and down throughout the land for the missing knight.

The days went by. Then one by one the search-parties returned. Anxiety grew; for not one of them brought back any news of Lancelot. When the last band rode into the torch-lit courtyard, weary, travel-stained, still without news, Gawain said:

"With the King's leave, and the Queen's, I will go in search of him myself."

Sir Kay, whose wounds no longer troubled him, said:

"And I with you."

All the freed knights of Logres begged leave to go with them.

Queen Guinevere said:

"Go, all of you, with my blessing."

King Bademagu said:

"Go, all of you, with mine, at dawn tomorrow."

As they sat at meat that night, a messenger came into the hall. On bended knee he gave a letter to King Bademagu, who called for his chaplain to open it and read it aloud to all the company.

The chaplain read:

"Sir Lancelot du Lake sends his greetings to King Bademagu as his kind host, and thanks him for all the courtesy and goodwill that he has shown him. Know that he is now safely arrived at King Arthur's Court. It is King Arthur's wish that the Queen, if she will consent, shall return to Camelot as soon as may be, in company with my lord Kay and my lord Gawain."

The letter bore Lancelot's signature.

The whole Court rejoiced at the news the letter brought; and it was decided that next day, as soon as it was light, Gawain and Kay and the freed knights of Logres, who had arranged to start on their search for Lancelot at dawn, should set out instead for King Arthur's Court, and that Queen Guinevere, with the freed ladies, should journey back to Camelot in their care.

So at dawn they mounted and set out, King Bademagu courteously conducting them to the borders of his kingdom. Here he parted from the Queen, from Gawain, from Kay and from all the rest of their company, with great friendship; and the party rode rejoicing on its homeward way.

News of their coming went before them; and the streets of Camelot, as they rode in, were crowded with citizens and countryfolk throwing flowers before their horses' hoofs and cheering with joy at their return, calling:

"Welcome home to our Queen Guinevere! Welcome to our lord Gawain, who has brought her back with many another captive lady, and freed for us many prisoners!"

Gawain saluted them courteously, and reined in his steed to reply:

"Friends, I have not earned this praise. It shames me, for I did not reach our Queen till she was already freed by my lord Lancelot."

A spokesman among the people called:

"Where is he, then, fair sir? For we do not see him with you."

"Where?" echoed Gawain. "He is here, with King Arthur, surely?"

"No, fair sir," the crowd answered. "He is not at Camelot, nor anywhere else in our country. Since our Lady was taken away, we have had no news of him."

And this they found to be true when they reached the Court. It was good beyond all telling to be home in Logres again; and every soul in the country, from King Arthur downwards, rejoiced at their return. Yet the letter which had recalled them had not been written by Lancelot.

Then by whom had it been written?

And where *was* Lancelot?

XIII. HOW THE KNIGHT OF THE CART FOUGHT AT A TOURNAMENT IN DISGUISE

HERE was Lancelot?

Lancelot was a prisoner in the house of Prince Meleagant's seneschal, for it was Meleagant who had sent his dwarf to decoy Lancelot into captivity, and it was Meleagant also who had forged Lancelot's letter.

Now in honour of Queen Guinevere's homecoming it was decided that a tournament should be held at Noanz. The news of this tournament spread far and wide, and in due course it reached the house of Prince Meleagant's seneschal, just when the seneschal was absent on Meleagant's affairs.

The seneschal's wife pitied Lancelot greatly, and to cheer him she told him of the tournament. But instead of being cheered by the news, he became even more sad and pensive.

Seeing this, she said to him:

"Sir, you neither eat nor drink, laugh nor make merry. Tell me why you are so troubled."

"Ah, Lady," replied Lancelot, "since I cannot be present where all the good knights in the world will be assembled, do not be surprised if I am sad."

"You mean the tournament at Noanz?" she asked.

"I would I might be there to fight in Queen Guinevere's honour," said Lancelot. "Had your husband been at home, I would have asked for leave to attend it on parole, and I do not doubt he would have granted it."

"Sir," she said, "he left you in my charge. But I would not dare to grant it. For Prince Meleagant would have my husband's life if you failed to return."

"Lady," he replied, "to you I would swear as solemn an oath as to him, an oath I would never break, to return at once to my prison here when the tournament was over."

The lady mused awhile.

"I accept your oath," she said at last.

Out of the seneschal's armoury she brought armour and harness and a vermilion shield, and chose a fine steed from his stable. Thus well armed and well mounted, and giving his word once more to return when the tournament was over, Lancelot rode away and out of the country, and so came to Noanz.

Here he took a small and lowly lodging outside the town, for he did not wish to lodge where he might be recognized. The town was crowded; all the houses were filled to overflowing; many knights had to be quartered in tents and pavilions, for five leagues around, and it was wonderful how many fair damsels were to be seen.

Knights were still arriving by tens, twenties, fifties, hundreds. As they assembled, their lances were like a wood; and around the ladies' grandstands you could see nothing but banners and standards.

When Lancelot entered the lists, disguised in the seneschal's armour with the vermilion shield, he was as good as twenty knights, so that everyone was asking:

"Who is this unknown knight who fights so well?"

Queen Guinevere, watching from the seat of honour in the ladies' stands, wondered, also. She thought she knew; but, to make sure, next day she sent one of her damsels to him with a message:

"Sir, my lady the Queen sends you word that you shall do your worst."

"Willingly, since that is her will," Lancelot replied.

And from then till the fighting ceased that evening he played a coward's part, so that all who had praised him earlier now looked at him with scorn.

But Queen Guinevere rejoiced, assured that this was Lancelot. And next day she sent the same damsel to him with a different message:

"Sir, my lady the Queen sends you word that you shall do your best."

Then Lancelot's feats with sword and lance were marvellous to behold. On every hand he made steeds stumble and knights fall. Every eye was upon him, and it was everywhere admitted that no other knight equalled the Knight with the Vermilion Shield.

When the tournament came to an end, the Knight with the Vermilion Shield was adjudged the victor, and Queen Guinevere awaited his approach to receive the prize from her fair hands. But the heralds sought for him in vain.

He had allowed his vermilion shield to fall where the press was thickest, and had ridden away so secretly that no-one saw him go. All the knights were disappointed, and all the damsels even more so; but most disappointed of all was Queen Guinevere.

Lancelot had kept the promise he had given to the seneschal's wife and had returned to his captivity.

XIV. HOW PRINCE MELEAGANT BUILT A TOWER TO IMPRISON THE KNIGHT OF THE CART

PRINCE MELEAGANT'S seneschal returned home some days before he was expected. When he sat down to meat and Lancelot did not come to table, he asked his wife:

"Where is the Knight of the Cart?"

And she confessed:

"I have allowed him to go to joust at the tourney at Noanz."

"Lady," he cried, "you could have done nothing more disastrous. I shall smart for this when my lord Meleagant hears of it."

"Do not be dismayed, fair sir," begged his wife. "Sir Lancelot swore to me by the saints to return as soon as the tourney was over."

"What man would keep such an oath once he was free?" the seneschal exclaimed. "I had better seek out my lord at once and make a clean breast of the matter."

And, rising from his untouched meal, he sent for a horse to be saddled and rode away to seek out Prince Meleagant, and told him the whole story.

When Prince Meleagant heard it, he grew red with anger.

"I am greatly displeased," he said, "at what your wife has done. I would not for anything have had this knight present at that tourney. It could well wreck all the plans I have made with so much care."

"What would you have me do now, my lord?" asked the seneschal. "Shall I send out in search of him?"

"There will be no need for that," replied Prince Meleagant. "He will not break his oath; he will return on the appointed day. When he does so, keep him strictly guarded. No longer allow him freedom of body. And send me word at once. Meanwhile I shall prepare him a closer confinement."

And he sent at once for the best stone-masons in the land, and bade them build him a tower, high and thick and well-founded, on a lonely rock in an arm of the sea off a deserted part of the coast.

When the seneschal reached his home, he found Lancelot already returned, and at once sent a messenger to Prince Meleagant with the news. From now on Lancelot was kept very closely guarded till the building of the tower was finished.

Then Prince Meleagant sent his men by night to his seneschal's house and had Lancelot bound and taken to the island secretly. And when he was in the tiny chamber at the top of the tower, the doorway at the foot was walled up, so that no opening remained except one small and narrow slit just below the roof, through which, in a basket he was to let down on a rope, Lancelot had to draw up, once a week, his poor and meagre fare of water and barley-bread.

When Prince Meleagant had Lancelot safely imprisoned in this lonely tower, he betook himself to Logres, to King Arthur's Court at Camelot – behold him now arrived! He strode arrogantly into the hall, and stood before King Arthur, and addressed him thus:

"King, I had appointed a combat to take place here in your presence. I offer myself to fight it, though I see nothing of Sir Lancelot, who had accepted my challenge. If he is present, let him now step forward and agree to meet me in single combat here a year from today."

Queen Guinevere, who was seated beside King Arthur, leaned towards him and said in a low voice:

"Sire, do you know who this knight is? It is Prince Meleagant, who wounded Kay and carried us both away to his own land."

King Arthur replied, in the same low tone:

"Lady, I understand. Also, I know full well that it was he who held so many of my people captive."

To Prince Meleagant he said:

"Sir, we are very sad because there is nothing known of Lancelot in all this land."

"Nevertheless," insisted Meleagant, "the Queen herself is witness, and so are many knights and ladies here, that if he does not meet my challenge, the Queen must be surrendered. He has one year of grace."

Then Gawain rose and said courteously:

"We will search for Lancelot, and, if God will, we shall find him yet, before the end of that year's grace is reached. But if he does not return before that day, I beg you to grant me this combat in his place."

96

"There is no knight in the world with whom I would rather fight excepting Lancelot,"

Prince Meleagant replied. "But bear in mind that if I do not fight with one of you two, or if I fight with either and win the combat, pledge has been given that I bear my fair booty away without any hindrance."

King Arthur having replied that this was so, Prince Meleagant turned and strode from the hall, well-pleased with the way his own dark plans were shaping.

XV. HOW A DAMSEL RELEASED THE KNIGHT OF THE CART FROM THE TOWER

TILL well-pleased with his plans, Prince Meleagant returned to his father's castle, and found him holding a joyous feast to mark his birthday. The tower and the courtyard were filled with a happy throng of knights and ladies. Sitting beside King Bademagu was his daughter, a damsel as good as her brother, Prince Meleagant, was proud and disdainful. This was that damsel who had begged of Lancelot the grisly boon of the head of the Knight of the Sword-Bridge, and who, when he granted it, had told him that at the appointed time he would be repaid beyond his imagining.

Prince Meleagant came towards them, strutting like a peacock.

"Father," he greeted King Bademagu, "has not that man cause for pride who is feared at King Arthur's Court?"

"That is a strange question, my son," replied the King mildly. "Tell me why you ask it."

"You will remember," said Prince Meleagant, "the terms on which I surrendered Queen Guinevere – that Sir Lancelot would fight with me again within a year of my challenging him. I have just journeyed to Camelot to throw down this challenge. The coward was not there; no-one knows where he has gone."

As King Bademagu remained silent, Prince Meleagant went on:

"Sir Gawain pledged his word to take his place if he did not return; and that pleases me. For it means that before the flowers bloom again I shall have slain one or other of the two best of Arthur's knights, all of whom I hate with my whole heart!"

"My son," said the King gently, "if you were but as gentle and generous as you are strong and formidable, there could be no better knight found. But you have a heart of wood, so hard that it has no place for sweetness or friendship. How otherwise could you speak in this way of the courteous Gawain? As for Lancelot, only a fool could suppose that that flower of knights has fled from you in fear. If he does not appear in answer to your challenge, it will be because he is dead or in some prison; and God forbid it should be either!"

Prince Meleagant, stung, flung fuming out of his father's presence, while his sister sat with bent head, lost in thought.

"May I be barred from God's blessing," she said to herself, "if I rest until I have some sure and certain news of Lancelot!"

Quietly she slipped away from her father's side and out of the castle. Mounting her tawny mule, she rode away without the company of knight or squire or groom. Taking the first path she found, she rode rapidly at random, up hill, down dale, through fen and forest, seeking always for some clue that would lead her to news of Lancelot.

More than a month had passed when one day, as she rode in a desert place, she saw a tower in the distance. It stood like a lifted finger, calling her to halt. She rode towards it; it drew her on; it led her down to the shore of an arm of the sea. Then she saw that it stood on a lonely rock in that sea.

She looked about her, left and right. There was no other dwelling in sight. But a boat was drawn up on the beach, and in it were oars and a water-cask.

She dismounted, and tied her mule to a wind-stunted thorn-tree. She entered the boat, and rowed to the rock. Her heart assured her that here was the end of her quest.

The tower was tall and strong and surely newly built. She left the boat and went so near to the tower that she could touch it with her hands. She walked all round it, but could find no entrance, only a place where clearly a doorway had been walled up. She gazed up, and saw how impregnable it was. To her amazement, there was no ladder, there were no steps, with which to scale it; its surface was broken by neither door nor window, but only by a narrow opening near the top.

She set her hands about her lips, and threw back her head, and called with all her heart:

"Lancelot! Lancelot!"

From the narrow opening near the top came a groan, and broken words:

"God! I thought I heard my name! Was that a spirit?"

The damsel drew in a deep breath, and called again:

"No spirit, Lancelot, but a damsel who once begged a boon of you and now repays it. Friend, up there, speak to one who is *your* friend!"

In the tiny tower-top cell, Lancelot rose painfully to his feet and staggered with feeble steps to the little opening. She drew backwards from the base of the tower till he could see her.

"Lancelot," she called up to him, "I have come to set you free. How can I get into this tower?"

"There is no way in," he told her. "The masons walled it up behind me."

"Then how," she asked, "do you get food and water?"

"When my jailers row across with it," he told her, "I let down a basket on a rope and haul it up."

"Is the rope long enough and strong enough," she asked next, "for you to escape by it?"

"Yes," he called back, "but the opening is too narrow."

"Wait, then," she called, "while I look for something to enlarge it."

He waited; and presently she hailed him joyfully:

"Lancelot, I have found a pick the masons left behind them. Let down your rope for it!"

You may be sure Lancelot did so quickly, and, when she had tied the pick to it, he as quickly hauled it up.

In his feeble state it was weary work pick-picking at the slit; but at last enough stone broke away for his gaunt frame to squeeze through.

Then down the rope he slid, into the damsel's arms. She made him lean on her, and so brought him to the boat. She rowed him across to where her mule stood waiting, and lifted him to its back. Then she led him by hidden paths to a secluded mansion of her own; and here she nursed him back to health, so tenderly that I cannot describe half the care she took, treating him as gently as if he had been her father.

So he who had been so feeble became once more strong and nimble; he who had been so haggard became once more handsome as an angel.

Some months had therefore passed when Lancelot said to the damsel one day:
"I have only God and yourself to thank for being restored to health and free in the open air again. Ought I not now to show my thanks to you both by riding out and using this health and freedom in knightly service?"

Then the damsel knew that the time for which she had been waiting was ripe – the time to tell him of how Prince Meleagant had thrown down his challenge at Camelot, and of how Lancelot's year of grace would soon be drawing to its close.

When she had told him, he was silent. Then he said:
"Sweet, gentle friend, have I your leave to go?"
"Go, Lancelot!" she replied.

The finest of armour, the finest of horses, she bestowed on him. And when they had embraced and commended each other to God, Lancelot rode away on his journey to Camelot.

XVI. HOW THE KNIGHT OF THE CART SAVED QUEEN GUINEVERE

HEN Lancelot in due course caught his first glimpse of the beloved towers of Camelot, Prince Meleagant, magnificently armed and mounted, had just ridden into the castle courtyard. The first thing he did, even before he entered the hall to bow the knee to King Arthur, was to seek out Gawain.

"Has Lancelot been found?" he asked, as if he did not know the truth. (As a matter of fact he did *not* know the truth, though he *thought* he knew it well enough.)

Gawain told him, as was true, that Lancelot had not been seen or even heard of either by himself or by any other of the knights of King Arthur's fellowship who had spent the whole of this year of grace in searching for him.

"Then the combat is between you and me," said Prince Meleagant with great satisfaction. "Which means that before the sun goes down, Queen Guinevere will be mine to take away."

Gawain, ever courteous, ignored Meleagant's insolence, and sent at once for his squires to come and arm him. He stood on a carpet of gold velvet while they did so, then mounted the spirited Spanish steed his grooms had brought from the royal stables. As he took his shield, a knight of most noble bearing rode into the courtyard on a steed as noble. He came towards them, dismounted, and raised his visor, so that his face was seen.

Gawain looked, then looked again. Behold, it was Lancelot!

If I am not wrong, Gawain was as much astonished as if Lancelot had fallen from the clouds. Dismounting, he rushed to embrace his long-lost friend. Both knights felt happy and at ease, for each had found again his best companion. I would not lie if I said they were so close that neither would wish to be chosen king unless he had the other with him.

King Arthur and all his fellowship came hastening to the courtyard when they heard that he for whom they had so long searched had returned to them safe and sound. They surrounded him, embracing him in turn with great rejoicing. Queen Guinevere, with all her ladies, quickly followed to welcome him with gracious words.

King Arthur said to Lancelot:

"Never have I had news of any man so welcome as the news of your return. I have had search made for you all summer and winter through. Tell me in what land you have tarried for so long a time."

"Indeed, fair sir," Lancelot told him, "I have been held captive by my challenger, and should still be so had not a pitiful damsel released me and nursed me back to health."

"Friend," said Gawain, "let me meet this challenge for you."

Lancelot replied:

"Not for all the wealth from Babylon to Ghent will I fail to meet that challenger whom I have to thank for this long year of harm and shame."

Prince Meleagant, standing by, amazed, almost beside himself, and coming near to fainting, fumed inwardly:

"Fool that I am to let Lancelot thus outwit me! In this combat he shall pay me a thousand times over for this discomfiture!"

You may be sure it was no warm welcome and no sparkling glances that Meleagant received when all this came to light. But his challenge had been accepted; the year of grace was at an end; Queen Guinevere must be defended, the combat must be fought.

So King Arthur said:

"Let us go down into the plain where the tower stands. It is the prettiest place this side of Ireland for a fight."

And down to the plain they all went. No-one, not even the youngest scullion in the castle kitchens, stayed behind.

There Queen Guinevere and all her ladies went up into the tower, from which they would have a fine view of the combat; for this tower, unlike the tower Prince Meleagant had built for Lancelot, was as full of windows as a fowling-net is full of holes.

Below the tower stood a sycamore tree as fair as any tree could be, with fresh green grass around it, and under it a clear spring of water, its bed shining like silver. Here King Arthur took his seat, with all his knights about him. And when the crowds had drawn back to leave an open space in the meadow, the heralds blew their trumpets, and their command rang out:

"Combatants, take your stands."

Prince Meleagant and Lancelot turned from each other, and spurred their steeds till they had each drawn back the distance of a bowshot. Then they turned again and urged their horses forward at such a speed that each knight's lance pierced the other's shield in passing. Both knights were bold and hardy; both horses were swift and finely bred. Passing each other, they returned again and yet again, making mighty thrusts till the cold steel reached the flesh.

Soon each bore the other to earth, and both horses ran riderless over hill and dale, kicking and biting each other. The two knights sprang to their feet, and, holding their shields before their faces, drew their swords. Prince Meleagant handled his with rare skill; but Lancelot was the finest swordsman at that time in the whole world.

The blows they rained on each other's painted shield and gold-barred helmet crushed and damaged them. The Prince Meleagant, now beside himself with rage, rushed on Lancelot to seize him, and opened himself to a mortal blow. Before he could even cry for mercy, he had fallen dead.

King Arthur, with a band of knights, came forward to relieve Lancelot of his armour and to lead him away to the bath and to fresh, fair garments. Right had prevailed. Queen Guinevere had been saved. The Knight of the Cart again took his place in King Arthur's fellowship, and the land of Logres was filled with thanksgiving and rejoicing.

SIR THOMAS MALORY AND HIS ENGLISH PROSE ·ROMANCES

SIR THOMAS MALORY AND HIS
15TH. CENTURY PROSE-ROMANCES

UR last story, *The Story of Sir Gareth*, comes from *Le Morte d'Arthur*, the most famous English book of Arthurian stories. It was written in English in the fifteenth century by Sir Thomas Malory while he was a "knight-prisoner" in the terrible London prison known as Newgate.

Le Morte d'Arthur is written in medieval English prose, into which Malory translated the various twelfth, thirteenth and fourteenth century French verse-romances, which make up most of the book. He tells us that he had meant to include Chrétien's *Knight of the Cart* among these, but that he had lost the French manuscript. (We can well imagine him having to leave behind some of his precious manuscripts in his hurry and distress when he was hustled away to his solitary stone cell.)

About *The Story of Sir Gareth* there is a mystery, for this story is not to be found in *any* foreign original. It is quite new; and Malory's way of telling it is also quite new. In it Malory keeps to one thread all through, instead of following the medieval method of intertwining so many threads that it is sometimes difficult for us today to keep them all in mind. In this story Malory builds a bridge from the medieval way of story-telling to our modern way.

Malory was still a prisoner when he finished his book in 1469, during the Wars of the Roses. At the end he writes:

"I pray you all, gentlemen and gentlewomen who read this book of Arthur and his knights, pray for me while I am alive, that God send me good deliverance, and when I am dead I pray you all to pray for my soul."

Printing had just been invented. In 1485, 15 years after Malory had finished it, Caxton, one of England's pioneer printers, brought out *Le Morte d'Arthur* as a printed book. It was the first book about King Arthur and his knights to be *printed* anywhere in the world.

With the coming of printing, the wonderful manuscripts which had been written by hand (that is what *manuscript* means) in medieval times went out of fashion; and the beautiful illuminations which had – also by hand – been drawn and coloured with so much love and artistry were replaced by woodcuts, out of which grew our modern black-and-white illustrations. (There is a woodcut of Gareth's arrival at the Court of King Arthur in Caxton's first printed edition of Malory's book).

So we can follow the descent of the Arthurian stories from the Welsh bards' songs chanted to their harp-music, through Marie de France's delicate rhymed lays, and on through Chrétien's verse-romances written to be recited, to Malory's prose, written to be read. With printed books instead of manuscripts, and with woodcuts instead of illuminations, the age-old stories of King Arthur's knights had come at last to earth.

THE STORY OF SIR GARETH

THE STORY OF SIR GARETH

I. HOW FAIRHANDS CAME TO KING ARTHUR'S COURT

ONE year King Arthur held the Feast of Pentecost at one of his castles called Kynk Kenadon, which was built on the sands near Wales. All the Knights of the Round Table were there, with Queen Guinevere and all her ladies.

As they all sat feasting, two men entered the hall, with a tall youth between them, leaning on their shoulders. He was richly dressed, and had beautiful hands; and he was a foot and a half taller than his companions.

When they came before the King, the youth stood upright and said:

"God bless you and all your fellowship, most noble King! I come to ask of you three gifts."

"Ask," replied King Arthur. "If I can grant them, they are already yours."

"My first is this, Sire," said the youth. "That you will give me food and drink for a year. And at the end of the year I will ask for the two other gifts."

"My fair son," said King Arthur, "this is a humble request. Ask for something better."

"Sire," said the youth, "this is all I ask for now."

"Then certainly you shall have food and drink," promised King Arthur. "Now tell me, what is your name?"

"Sire, I cannot tell you," said the youth.

"I marvel much," said the King, "that you do not know your name, for you are one of the noblest-looking young men I ever saw."

Then King Arthur sent for Sir Kay, his Steward of the Royal Household; and he bade him give the young man the best of food and drink and lodge him as though he were a lord's son.

"No need for that," said Sir Kay. "If he had been gently born, he would have asked for a horse and armour. I will put him to work in the kitchen, and he shall have fat broth every day. And as he has no name, I will give him the name of Fairhands, for those hands of his will not stay so beautiful when he is doing the work of a scullion."

Then the two men who had brought the youth took their leave, and Kay mocked Fairhands and sent him to sit and eat among the kitchen-knaves near the hall door. Sir Lancelot and Sir Gawain were angry with Sir Kay, and invited Fairhands to come and eat with them in their own chambers; but he replied gently and courteously that as the King had put him in Sir Kay's charge, he would do whatever Sir Kay commanded.

So he was put into the kitchen, and there he worked with the other kitchen-knaves and slept where they slept. And for a whole year he did meekly and gladly whatever Sir Kay ordered him to do. But whenever the knights were jousting, he loved to watch if his tasks left him free to do so. And at contests of skill among the serving-men and boys he was always the victor, and could throw the bar two yards further than any of the others.

Then Sir Kay would say mockingly:

"What think you now of my new kitchen-knave?"

So the year passed, and the Feast of Pentecost came round again, when Fairhands was to ask King Arthur for his other two gifts.

II. HOW A DAMSEL CAME SEEKING HELP FROM KING ARTHUR, AND HOW FAIRHANDS WAS GRANTED THE ADVENTURE

T this second Pentecost King Arthur held his feast in most royal fashion at his castle at Caerleon-on-Usk in Wales. And while he and his knights, with Queen Guinevere and her ladies, were seated at table, a damsel came into the hall.

"Sire," she said, bending the knee to King Arthur, "my sister is besieged in her castle by an evil knight. And because your knights are the noblest in the world, she has sent me to ask for your help."

"Lady," replied King Arthur, "tell me your sister's name, and the name of her castle, and the name of the knight who is besieging her."

"Sire," she said, "my sister's name I must not tell you, nor where she dwells; but the knight is called Sir Ironside."

"I do not know this knight," said King Arthur.

"Sire," said Sir Gawain, "I have heard of him. He is one of the most dangerous knights in the world."

"Damsel," said King Arthur, "any of my knights here would do their utmost to rescue your sister. But unless we know her name and where she dwells, they cannot go with you."

"Then I must seek further," replied the damsel.

Then Fairhands rose from his lowly seat among the kitchen-knaves by the hall door, and came and stood before the King, and bowed, and said:

"Lord King, God thank you for granting my first gift. I have been a year in your kitchen, and all that time I have had food and drink from you. Now the time has come for me to ask you for my other two gifts."

"Ask on, fair son," said the King.

"Sire," said Fairhands, "the first gift I would ask is that you grant me the adventure of this damsel, for it belongs to me."

"I grant it," said the King.

"Then, Sire," continued Fairhands, "the second gift I would beg of you is that you will let Sir Lancelot ride after me and make me a knight as soon as in his eyes I merit knighthood."

"I grant this, also," said the King.

By now the damsel was beside herself with rage.

"What?" she cried. "Am I offered no champion but a scullion?"

And she rushed from the hall, and mounted her steed in the courtyard, and rode away from the castle at full gallop.

Then a groom came in, and knelt before the King, and told him:

"Sire, a dwarf has come, riding a noble horse laden with rich armour. And he says they are for Fairhands the kitchen-knave."

Everyone was astonished at this news. But they were even more astonished when Fairhands went out and donned the armour and came back to take his leave of King Arthur. For there were few knights in the hall better to look upon than he was then.

Many went out into the courtyard to see him mount his horse, take the dwarf up behind him, and gallop after the damsel.

"What a noble charger he rides!" cried one.

"See, its trappings are of cloth-of-gold!" cried a second.

"But alas, he has neither spear nor shield!" cried a third.

But Sir Kay cried:

"I will ride after my kitchenboy, and see whether he will still know me for his better!"

III. HOW FAIRHANDS OVERCAME SIR KAY AND WAS KNIGHTED BY SIR LANCELOT

S O Sir Kay donned his armour, and mounted his horse, and took his spear, and called his squire to follow him, and rode after Fairhands.

And, seeing this, Sir Lancelot also donned his armour and mounted his steed, and rode with his squire after Sir Kay.

And just as Fairhands overtook the damsel, Sir Kay overtook Fairhands.

"Fairhands!" he shouted. "You with no thought above bread and broth! Do you not know me, sirrah?"

Then Fairhands put down his dwarf on the ground, and turned his horse, and said quietly:

"Yes, Sir Kay. I know you well for an ungentle knight. Therefore, beware of me!"

Then, spear in rest, Sir Kay rode straight at Fairhands. And Fairhands, having no spear, drew his sword and rode as fast towards Sir Kay. And with his sword he thrust aside Sir Kay's spear and smote him in the side, so that he fell from his saddle, sorely wounded.

Then Fairhands alighted, and took Sir Kay's shield and spear, and called to Sir Kay's squire to tend his master's wound, and bade his own dwarf mount Sir Kay's horse and follow him.

As Fairhands was riding away, Sir Lancelot overtook him and called to him, inviting him courteously to joust with him. As courteously, Fairhands accepted. He gladly turned his horse, and they joined combat.

They rushed together like two boars, and Sir Lancelot marvelled at Fairhands' strength, for he fought more like a giant than a man. When they had borne each other to the ground, Sir Lancelot called out:

"Fairhands, fight not so fiercely! You and I have no quarrel."

"Truly, that is so," Fairhands replied. "But it does me good to feel your might."

So then they both ceased fighting, and sheathed their swords, and each clasped the other's hand in friendship.

"Truly," gasped Sir Lancelot, "it was all I could do to save myself from you unashamed!"

"Think you then, Sir Lancelot," Fairhands asked, eagerly, "that I may soon stand a proved knight?"

"I think you do that already," replied Sir Lancelot.

"Then," cried Fairhands, "I pray you, make me one now!"

"Before I can do that," replied Sir Lancelot, "I must know your name and lineage."

"I will gladly tell you," said Fairhands. "But you must keep it secret."

"I will tell it to none," Sir Lancelot assured him, "until it is openly known."

Then Fairhands told him:

"My name is Gareth. My father is King Lot of Orkney. My mother, Queen Morgawse, is King Arthur's sister. Sir Gawain is my brother. He saw me last fifteen years ago, when I was a small boy."

"Ah," cried Sir Lancelot, "I was sure from the first that you were of noble blood and that you came to King Arthur's Court for more than food and drink."

Then Sir Lancelot knighted Fairhands, and embraced him, and they parted in firm fellowship. Sir Lancelot returned to King Arthur's Court with the wounded Sir Kay and their two squires, while Fairhands, with his dwarf, rode on after the damsel.

IV.   HOW FAIRHANDS OVERCAME THE BLACK KNIGHT

A S soon as Fairhands overtook the damsel, she began to lash him with her tongue:

"Turn back, you dirty kitchen-knave! You reek of grease and tallow. Get you gone! What help can such as *you* bring my sister? You are nothing but a turner of spits and a washer of ladles!"

Fairhands bore her anger patiently.

"Damsel," said he, "say what you will to me, you cannot drive me away from you; for I have received your adventure from King Arthur himself, and I will finish it even if I die in doing so."

"That will be sooner than you think," she taunted him. "For not all the broth that you have ever supped will save you when you meet the knight that you have soon to face!"

"I will stay with you all the same," Fairhands replied. "Serve me as badly as you will; wherever you go I will still follow you."

So they rode on, and the damsel never ceased to chide him. But Fairhands never ceased to bear her chiding cheerfully.

Presently she said:

"Soon we shall come to the first Perilous Passage. Turn back or die, kitchen-knave!"

But Fairhands rode on beside her tranquilly, till they came to a hawthorn bush on which there hung a black banner and a black shield. Beside it stood a great black horse, bearing a knight in black armour, with a black spear in his hand and a squire standing behind him.

"Damsel," called the Black Knight, "is this knight your champion?"

"Not so, fair sir," she replied. "He is but a kitchen-knave, fed in King Arthur's kitchen for charity. I cannot get rid of him. I would rejoice if you would rid me of his company."

"Sirrah," thundered the Black Knight, turning to Fairhands, "depart from this damsel. It is not seemly for a kitchen-knave to ride with so high-born a lady."

"Sir," said Fairhands, "be that as it may, this passage she must pass, and my dwarf and I with her."

"I will take his horse and armour from him," the Black Knight told the damsel, "and he can make his own way back on foot."

"Sir Knight," said Fairhands, "you make very free with my horse and armour. If you wish to take them, you must win them in fair fight.

"Say you so, kitchen-knave?" cried the Black Knight. "Then let us see what you can do to keep them."

Then they came together like thunder, while the damsel rode on her way. The Black Knight's spear broke, and Fairhands' spear ran him through, so that the Black Knight fell from his horse. When Fairhands alighted from his own horse, the Black Knight was already dead.

Then Fairhands donned the Black Knight's armour, and mounted the Black Knight's horse, and committed the Black Knight's body to the care of his squire, and rode on after the damsel, and his own dwarf rode on after him.

"Away, scullion!" the damsel greeted him. "Get out of the wind, for you stink of the kitchen."

"Maiden," he replied, "I will not leave you till this adventure is achieved."

"Do not be too sure," she warned him tauntingly. "For we have reached the second Perilous Passage, and I see one coming who will soon rid me of you!"

V. HOW FAIRHANDS OVERCAME THE GREEN KNIGHT

T HEN Fairhands looked and saw a knight come pricking out of the greenwood towards them. He wore green armour and rode a horse in green trappings, and he bore a green shield and a green spear.

"Welcome, Lady!" he greeted the damsel. "Is this my brother the Black Knight who rides with you?"

"It is not, and that is a thousand pities," replied the damsel. "This is a kitchen-knave who has unhorsed and slain your brother."

"Ah, traitor!" cried the Green Knight. "For that you yourself shall die!"

So he and Fairhands turned their horses to face each other and rushed to meet each other with all their might, so that their spears broke in their hands. Then they drew their swords, and each struck the other such mighty blows that they were both unhorsed.

Then the damsel cried to the Green Knight:

"My lord, for shame that you were ever made a knight, to see a kitchen-lad overmatch you as the weed overgrows the corn!"

At this, Fairhands dealt the Green Knight such a buffet on his helmet with his sword that he fell on his knees, yielding to Fairhands and craving mercy.

"If this damsel bids me show mercy," said Fairhands, "gladly will I do so."

"Fie upon you, kitchen-knave!" cried the damsel. "That will I never do, for never will I be indebted to you."

"Then a brave knight must die for lack of a word from a lady," said Fairhands, slowly lifting his sword as if about to slay him.

"Alas, maiden!" cried the Green Knight. "Let me not die when one fair word would save me!"

Then the damsel said to Fairhands:

"Let be, you knave! Slay him not!"

"Damsel," replied Fairhands, "your charge is to me a pleasure!"

Then Fairhands sheathed his sword, and the Green Knight knelt before him and became his man, doing homage with his sword.

But the damsel cried:

"Fie upon you, that any good knight should be obedient to a kitchen-knave!"

"Not I alone," said the Green Knight to Fairhands, "but the fifty knights of my household shall also do you service."

Then the Green Knight begged them to lodge with him that night; and the next morning he and his fifty knights rode some way with them through the greenwood.

And as they parted, the Green Knight said:

"My lord Fairhands, I and these fifty knights will be always at your summons, early and late, to go wherever you may send us."

"That is well said," replied Fairhands courteously. "It would be well done if you would seek King Arthur at the next Feast of Pentecost and yield yourselves to him."

"This we will do," promised the Green Knight.

Then they parted in friendly fashion; and Fairhands and the damsel continued on their way, the damsel still chiding him.

"Cast away your spear and shield, kitchen-knave, and flee while you can," she cried. "For we are now drawing near to the third Perilous Passage; and this no kitchen-knave could pass."

"Damsel," he replied, "it would be a pity to turn back now, when I have ridden so long with you."

"Well," said the damsel, "turn soon you will, whether you will or not."

And so the damsel and Fairhands and his dwarf still rode on together.

VI. HOW FAIRHANDS OVERCAME THE RED KNIGHT

RESENTLY they came out of the greenwood, and saw before them a tall tower, and on its walls many knights passing to and fro, and before it a wide meadow.

Now the lord of the tower was standing at a window, and from it he saw a damsel, a knight and a dwarf ride out of the greenwood.

"I must joust with that knight," said he; and he armed and rode out to meet them; and his armour and his horse-trappings and his shield and his spear were all red.

When he drew near to them, he recognised Fairhands' black armour and black horse as his brother's; and he called out in greeting:

"Well met, brother! What errand brings you here?"

"Nay, nay, Sir Knight," replied the damsel, "this is not your noble brother, but only a low-born scullion from King Arthur's kitchen."

"All the same," said the Red Knight, "I will joust with him since he is here."

"I pray you may overcome him," said the damsel. "For otherwise I shall never be quit of him."

So Fairhands and the Red Knight rode apart, then turned and came together with all their might; and they were so well-matched and fought together for so long that at last the damsel called out:

"Red Knight, never let a kitchen-knave endure so long against you!"

At this the Red Knight redoubled his strokes, and Fairhands redoubled his own, so that it was wonderful to see the strong battle. But in the end Fairhands struck the Red Knight to the earth, and the Red Knight yielded to him and craved mercy.

"Mercy you shall willingly have," said Fairhands, "if my damsel gives the word."

And this time the damsel said at once:

"Let be, Fairhands. Slay him not."

Then Fairhands sheathed his sword, and the Red Knight knelt in homage and became his man.

"And not I alone," said the Red Knight, "but the three score knights of my household shall also do your service."

Then the Red Knight begged them to lodge with him in his tower that night; and next morning he and his three score knights rode with them the next part of their way.

And as they parted, the Red Knight said:

"My lord Fairhands, I and these three score knights will be always at your summons, early and late, to go wherever you may send us."

"That is well said," replied Fairhands, courteously. "It would be well done if you would seek King Arthur at the next Feast of Pentecost and yield yourselves to him."

"This we will do," the Red Knight promised.

Then they parted in friendly fashion, and the damsel and Fairhands and the dwarf continued on their way.

VII. HOW FAIRHANDS OVERCAME THE BLUE KNIGHT

S they rode on together, the damsel continued her chiding, till presently Fairhands said:

"Damsel, you are uncourteous to rebuke me as you do. When you see me beaten by a better knight, then may you bid me go from you in shame. But till then I will not depart from you. And till then, I pray you, rebuke me no more."

"Well," said the damsel, "that will not be long, for soon you will meet a knight who will pay you all your wages. See, there is his pavilion, where he waits to joust with any knight who comes."

Then Fairhands saw before him a great tilting-ground, and at its entrance a most lordly pavilion of dark blue silk, and clustered about it many tents. The knight who rode out from the pavilion to meet them was clad in dark blue armour, and his shield and his spear and his horse-trappings were all of the same dark blue.

"You will find him the boldest and most dangerous knight," said the damsel, "that ever you looked upon."

"That may well be," said Fairhands, "but in this tilting-ground will I stay till I see him prone under his shield."

"Fie, fie!" cried the damsel. "That ever a kitchen-boy should so blow his own horn! You will do well to flee while you can."

"Nay," said Fairhands. "Here I will stay, and here I will fight as long as my life lasts."

Then the damsel said, speaking more gently:

"I pray you, save yourself while you may; for this is the last Perilous Passage before we come to the siege of my sister's castle. And I am in sore dread that if you stay and fight this knight you will be slain."

"Damsel," said Fairhands, "have no doubt that by the grace of God I shall defeat this knight and we shall pass this Perilous Passage as we have passed the others."

"I marvel," said the damsel, "what manner of man you are, so shamefully have I used you, and so courteously have you borne my ill-usage. Forgive me all the mis-sayings that I have mis-said against you."

"Damsel," said Fairhands, "since you now speak such fair words to me, it gladdens my heart greatly."

Then a messenger came to meet them from the Blue Knight, to ask in courteous fashion whether they came in war or in peace. And Fairhands sent back a courteous answer that he came to joust, in order that he and the damsel and his dwarf might pass this Perilous Passage.

Then Fairhands and the Blue Knight pricked on their steeds, and met so mightily that both their spears were splintered and both their horses fell dead. Then they fought on foot with sword and shield, and the battle was even between them until Fairhands smote the Blue Knight so sore a blow upon the helm that he was beaten to his knees and yielded himself to Fairhands and craved mercy at his hands.

Then the damsel also came and prayed Fairhands to spare his life.

"Most gladly," replied Fairhands. "It would be a thousand pities if such a noble knight must die."

"I thank you both, gentle knight and gentle damsel," said the Blue Knight. "Fair sir, you shall have homage both of me and of the hundred knights under me. We will be always at your summons, early and late, to go wherever you may send us."

"That is well said," replied Fairhands courteously. "It would be well done if you would seek King Arthur at the next Feast of Pentecost and yield yourselves to him."

"This we will do," promised the Blue Knight.

Then he begged them to lodge that night in his pavilion, and next morning he gave Fairhands a noble steed to replace the one killed in their jousting.

Then they parted in friendly fashion; and as they did so, the Blue Knight said to the damsel:

"Is not your name Linet?"

"It is, sir," she replied.

Then he asked further:

"And are you not sister to Dame Lyonesse, who is besieged in the Castle Perilous?"

"I am, sir," she replied again.

Now that was the first time Fairhands heard the names of the damsel he was riding with, or that of the lady he was riding to free, or that of the castle in which she was besieged.

VIII.   HOW FAIRHANDS OVERCAME SIR IRONSIDE AND RAISED THE SIEGE OF THE CASTLE PERILOUS

FAIRHANDS and the damsel Linet rode on through a fair forest till they came out of it and saw before them a plain on which stood a great castle. About the castle were many tents and pavilions, and many knights riding to and fro, and much smoke and noise.

As they drew nearer, Fairhands saw how on many trees hung dead knights, richly armed, with their shields about their necks and their gilt spurs on their heels.

"What can this mean?" exclaimed Fairhands.

"Fair sir," said the damsel Linet, "do not let this grisly sight discourage you. These are all knights who came to the siege to rescue my sister. Sir Ironside, the knight who will not let her come forth from her castle till she promises to marry him, has overcome all these knights in single combat, and then put them, each in turn, to this shameful death."

"Jesu defend me," said Fairhands, "from such a villainous end!"

They came to a sycamore tree, and on it hung a great horn.

"If any knight blows this horn," said the damsel Linet, "Sir Ironside will arm and come forth from his pavilion to do battle with him."

Then Fairhands spurred his horse to the sycamore tree and blew the horn so loudly that the castle rang with its echoes, and knights ran out of the tents, and those within the castle thronged the walls and windows, to see who blew the horn.

Then Sir Ironside came riding forth from his pavilion, armed from top to toe; and everything about him – horse and armour, shield and spear – was blood-red.

"See, sir," said Linet to Fairhands, "here comes your enemy. And there at her window stands my sister, watching you."

"Where?" asked Fairhands.

"There," said Linet, and pointed to a window at the front of the castle.

Fairhands looked up at the window, and the lady standing there curtseyed to the floor, holding up both her hands.

"She is the fairest lady I ever saw," said Fairhands. "I will take her for my lady, and I will fight for her right gladly."

Then Sir Ironside called out to him:

"Sir Knight, leave your looking at the lady, and look at me instead. That lady is mine, and to keep her mine I have fought many battles."

"They would seem to have been labour wasted," replied Fairhands, "since she still bars her castle doors against you."

Then they came together with all their might, and both fought so doughtily that all who were watching, both within the castle and without, said to each other:

"Never before have we seen Sir Ironside so well matched!"

When each had unhorsed the other, they drew their swords and fought on foot, running at each other like two fierce lions, till at last Fairhands smote Sir Ironside so lustily on the helm that he felled him to the ground, then knelt upon him and unlaced his helm to slay him.

Then the vanquished knight called out in a loud voice:

"Ah, noble knight! I yield me to your mercy!"

But Fairhands replied:

"What mercy did you show these forty knights you hanged so shamefully?"

Then from the tents and pavilions came running many knights and knelt before Fairhands, pleading:

"Noble knight, do not slay him, but take him as your prisoner. For if you slay him, then all his misdeeds can never be undone. Spare his life and we will all become your men and do homage to you with him."

Then said Fairhands:

"I will spare his life on the following terms: First he shall go to the castle and yield himself to the grace of my lady, Dame Lyonesse, and beg her forgiveness. And at the Feast of Pentecost he shall go to the Court of King Arthur, and put himself in his mercy."

And all this the vanquished knight undertook to do; and he and all his company knelt and made their homage and fealty to Fairhands.

"Fair sir and our lord," said Sir Ironside, "I and these three hundred knights will always be at your service, early and late, to go wherever you may send us."

Then the damsel Linet came and unarmed them both and staunched their blood and searched their wounds and bound these up with healing balsams. And for ten days she tended their hurts in the pavilion of the vanquished knight.

As soon as Sir Ironside's wounds were healed, he and all his company parted from Fairhands in friendly fashion, and rode up to the castle. There Sir Ironside yielded himself to its lady, Dame Lyonesse, and begged and received her forgiveness, and made recompense for all the harm that he had done her.

Then he and his company rode away to his own castle, taking down all the tents that had covered the plain except Sir Ironside's pavilion. In this he left Fairhands, in the care of his dwarf and the damsel Linet. And here Linet nursed Fairhands' wounds a few days longer.

IX.   HOW DAME LYONESSE SENT FAIRHANDS AWAY AND SIR GRINGAMORE STOLE FAIRHANDS' DWARF

AS soon as Fairhands' wounds were healed, he told Linet how greatly he desired to see her sister, Dame Lyonesse.

"Sir," she said, "I also greatly desire that you should see her."

So Fairhands donned his armour and mounted his horse and rode from the pavilion to the castle, his dwarf riding behind him.

But when he came to the barbican, he found the portcullis down and the drawbridge up, and the gate guarded by armed men, who told him respectfully:

"Sir, we may not suffer you to enter."

Then Fairhands looked up at the window at which he had seen Dame Lyonesse before his duel with Sir Ironside; and there he saw her again. She looked down on him from on high, calling sweetly:

"Go your ways, Sir Fairhands, and seek adventure for twelve months and a day. After that you shall hear new tidings."

"Alas, fair lady!" cried Fairhands. "Have I deserved that you should show me this strangeness? I had thought I had bought your kindness with part of the best blood of my body."

"Fair courteous knight," she replied gently, "do not be displeased, but go your way now and win yet more fame and honour. And trust me; I shall be true to you meanwhile."

With that she curtseyed and turned away from the window. And Fairhands turned his horse in great heaviness of heart, and rode away from the castle and across the plain, his dwarf close behind him. He rode furiously and not knowing where he rode, till, as evening drew on, he came to a great water. Beside this he dismounted, and lay down on the hard ground, and put his head on his shield, and said to his dwarf:

"Watch while I sleep awhile, and have a care our horses do not stray."

Now as soon as Fairhands had ridden away from the castle, Dame Lyonesse had called her brother, Sir Gringamore, and had begged him to ride after Fairhands.

"If you love me, dear brother," she said, "wait till you find him sleeping; for I am sure that in his heaviness he will soon lie down and sleep. Then quietly steal away his dwarf and ride swiftly with him to your own castle. Linet and I will meet you there; till we come, hold him in safe keeping."

"But, sister," replied Sir Gringamore, "why do you want the dwarf?"

"He will know his master's lineage," Dame Lyonesse explained, "and what his true name is. For, good brother, till I know these things I shall never be merry of heart."

"Sister," said Sir Gringamore, "since this is so, I will do as you say."

So he donned his armour and rode swiftly after Fairhands till, as evening drew on, he came to a great water; and here he saw Fairhands lying with closed eyes, his head on his shield; and nearby his dwarf was sitting, keeping watch over the horses.

Then Sir Gringamore came quietly, and, leaning sideways from his saddle, snatched up the drowsy dwarf, tucked him under his arm, and rode with him towards his own castle as fast as his steed could carry them both.

And all the time the dwarf was yelling lustily:

"Master! Master! Help! Help!"

His cries startled the drowsy Fairhands wide awake. He leapt to his feet, and was just in time to see a knight riding swiftly away with the struggling dwarf tucked under his arm. Hastily he donned his helm and buckled his shield, and was away after them like the wind, the dwarf's riderless horse keeping pace with his own.

The dwarf's repeated cries led him up hill and down dale, over moor and marsh, till the track he was following met and ended in a wide green way. And now he did not know whether to turn to the left or to the right, for he could see no rider and could hear no cries. But as he reined in his horse, listening and glancing both ways, he saw a poor countryman trudging towards him, bent under a heavy load of kindling-wood.

Fairhands saluted him kindly, and asked:

"Has a knight passed you, riding like the wind, with a dwarf under his arm?"

"Indeed, yes, sir," the old man replied. "It was a knight I know well – Sir Gringamore. His castle lies but a few miles away. This green way I have just come along will lead you straight to it."

Then Fairhands thanked and rewarded him, and rode swiftly towards the castle, and he did not draw rein till he reached it and could hear the guards upon its walls.

X.   HOW FAIRHANDS GOT BACK HIS DWARF AND FOUND HIS LADY

HEN Sir Gringamore reached his castle with the dwarf, Dame Lyonesse and Linet had just ridden across the drawbridge. Leaving Linet to oversee the making ready of their chambers, Dame Lyonesse at once began to question the dwarf as to his master's true name and lineage. "Why, Lady," said the dwarf. "I will tell you these matters right willingly. My master is a king's son and a queen's. His father is King Lot of Orkney. His mother, Queen Morgawse, is King Arthur's sister. My master's true name is Sir Gareth of Orkney."

"Are you content now, sister?" asked Sir Gringamore.

"Truly content, brother," she replied.

"Lady," continued the dwarf, "now that I have told you what you asked, I pray you give me leave to return to my master. For he will never go out of these parts till he has me again. And if you make him angry, he will do you all much harm."

"After those dire threats," said Sir Gringamore, laughing, "let us all go to dinner."

But hardly had they sat down to table when Fairhands rode up to the barbican with his dwarf's horse beside him and with his drawn sword in his hand. He called so loudly that the whole castle could hear him:

"Sir Gringamore, you traitor knight, give me back my dwarf!"

Then Sir Gringamore, laughing, rose from the table, and went to the window, and called back down to him:

"Sir Gareth, leave your shouting! It will not get you back your dwarf!"

"Then, coward knight," Fairhands called up to him, "bring him with you and do battle with me for him. For I will not go from here until I have my dwarf!"

Dame Lyonesse, also laughing, said to Sir Gringamore:

"Dear brother, I would he had his dwarf again. Now the dwarf has told me all I wished to know, I would not keep him from him. For it is Sir Gareth who has delivered me from Sir Ironside, and I love him more than all other knights alive. How I long to speak with him again!"

"Well, sister," replied Sir Gringamore, turning, "now I know your will, I will bring him into the castle, and you shall speak with him all you wish."

"But not as Dame Lyonesse of the Castle Perilous," she said. "I would wish him to think me some other strange lady."

"You shall be obeyed, sister," said Sir Gringamore, amused; and he went down to the barbican and greeted Fairhands with welcoming words:

"Sir Gareth, let me amend what I have done and said amiss. I pray you alight from your horse, and enter my castle, and enjoy such cheer as my sister and I can make you."

"Shall I have my dwarf?" asked Fairhands, obstinately. "*I must have my dwarf!*"

"Your dwarf you shall have," promised Sir Gringamore, courteously. "See, here he comes to meet you!"

Then Fairhands sheathed his sword and dismounted; and his dwarf came forward to greet him gladly and to lead away his master's horse and his own with him.

"Ah, my small fellow!" Fairhands cried. "Into what marshes and mires you have led me!"

Then he was led by the hand to a chamber, where maidens courteously unarmed him; and when he had bathed and was clad in a rich fur mantle, he was brought to Sir Gringamore in the hall.

Then into the hall swept Dame Lyonesse, arrayed like a princess, and welcomed him with warm glances and fair words. And Fairhands said to himself:

"I would that the lady of the Castle Perilous were as beautiful and forthcoming as this lady is!"

For as soon as he saw her, he began to love her.

So then they sat down again to table, and Fairhands with them, but not Linet, because Fairhands would know her again. And after supper the evening passed with games and pastimes, singing and dancing, mirth and minstrelsy. And the more Dame

Lyonesse and Fairhands beheld each other, the more they loved each other.

At midnight, when they all parted, Sir Gringamore drew Dame Lyonesse into a chamber, and said to her:

"Fair sister, you have told me that you love this knight more than all other knights alive."

"That is so," she replied. "And further, I am more beholden to him than to any other man."

"It is plainly to be seen that he is drawn to you," Sir Gringamore went on. "But his duty is towards the Lady of the Castle Perilous. My counsel to you is to tell him that you and that lady are one."

"Brother," said Dame Lyonesse, "my heart agrees with your counsel. I will tell him the whole truth tomorrow."

So next day she told Fairhands all — that she was that same lady of the Castle Perilous for whom he had done battle, and that it was she who had caused her brother to steal away his dwarf, so that she might learn his name and lineage.

"When I sent you from me I promised you new tidings," she said. "And these are those tidings, that I love you as well as you love me, and better if better can be!"

"Ah, lady," cried Fairhands, "there lives not a gladder man than I this day!"

Then Dame Lyonesse sent to bid her sister Linet to join them, and when Fairhands saw her again he was even more joyful. And they all made merry together.

Then Fairhands and Dame Lyonesse plighted their troth, and each promised to love and never to fail while their lives lasted.

Then Sir Gringamore said to Fairhands:

"As long as it pleases you, you shall sojourn with us here, and my sisters and I will make you all the good cheer we can."

And Fairhands gladly accepted, and they all four lived joyfully together in Sir Gringamore's castle till the Feast of Pentecost.

XI. HOW KING ARTHUR HELD A FEAST, AND OF THOSE WHO CAME TO IT

OW that year King Arthur held the Feast of Pentecost at his castle at Caerleon-on-Usk. And while the King and his knights, with Queen Guinevere and her ladies, sat at table, there came into the hall a knight in green armour, and with him a company of fifty knights. And they all knelt before King Arthur.

"Lord King," said the Green Knight, "I was overcome in single combat by a knight who bade me come and yield myself to you at this Feast of Pentecost. So, Sire, I have come, and with me my fifty knights."

"Sirs," said the King, "you are welcome. Who was this knight who sent you?"

"Sire," said the Green Knight, "I do not know him. But he is very young and very tall, and he had a damsel with him, and she called him Fairhands."

At this the King and all his Court (except Sir Lancelot) were much astonished.

Even as they were talking, there came into the hall a knight in red armour, and with him a company of three score knights. And they all knelt before King Arthur. "Lord King," said the Red Knight, "I was overcome in single combat by a knight who bade me come and yield myself to you at this Feast of Pentecost. So, Sire, I have come, and with me my three score knights."

"Sirs," said the King, "you are welcome. Who was this knight who sent you?"

"Sire," said the Red Knight, "I do not know him. But he is very young and very tall, and he had a damsel with him, and she called him Fairhands."

At this the King and all his Court (except Sir Lancelot) were again astonished.

Even as they were talking, there came into the hall a knight in blue armour, and with him a company of a hundred knights. And they all knelt before King Arthur. "Lord King," said the Blue Knight, "I was overcome in single combat by a knight who bade me come and yield myself to you at this Feast of Pentecost. So, Sire, I have come; and with me my hundred knights."

"Sirs," said the King, "you are welcome. Who was this knight who sent you?"

"Sire," said the Blue Knight, "I do not know him. But he is very young and very tall, and he had with him a damsel, and she called him Fairhands."

At this the King and all his Court (except Sir Lancelot) were even more astonished.

And as they were still talking, and the three brothers – the Green Knight, the Red Knight and the Blue Knight – were greeting one another, Sir Ironside came into the hall, with his company of three hundred knights. And they all knelt before King Arthur.

"Lord King," said Sir Ironside, "I was overcome in single combat by a knight who bade me come and yield myself to you at this Feast of Pentecost. So, Sire, I have come, and with me my three hundred knights."

"Sirs," said the King, "you are welcome. Who was this knight who sent you?"

"Sire," said Sir Ironside, "he is called Sir Fairhands, and he is the first knight who has ever had the better of me in thirty years. For I am that Sir Ironside who has long been one of the most evil and dangerous knights in the world."

"Ah, Sir Ironside," said King Arthur, "Sir Gawain has told me you have long been a foe to good knights; but now I trust to God that you will be their friend."

"Sire," replied Sir Ironside, "I have promised Sir Fairhands never again to use such shameful customs."

"I marvel much," said King Arthur, "how an untried youth could have proved himself such a noble knight so swiftly!"

"You would not, Sire," said Sir Lancelot, "if you knew from what family he came."

"Ah!" cried the King. "It would sound as if you know his true name and lineage?"

"I could not have knighted him otherwise," Sir Lancelot pointed out. "But he required me not to speak of these matters until they are known openly."

Then they all went to table and were served in the best manner; and while they were still feasting, there was a great clatter of horse-hoofs and rumbling of wheels in the courtyard, and the King's gatekeeper came in.

"Sire," he said, kneeling to King Arthur, "your royal sister, Queen Morgawse of Orkney, is here with many knights and ladies!"

Then Queen Morgawse entered the hall with her train of lords and ladies, and King Arthur rose to receive her. And Sir Gawain, who was her eldest son, left the table, to kneel before her and ask her blessing. And she bent and embraced him fondly and with tears.

"For," said she, "it is fifteen years since I last saw you!"

Then she turned to King Arthur, crying shrilly:

"Brother, what have you done with my son, Gareth, that is so young and that was my joy?"

"Sister," replied King Arthur, "I know nothing of him."

"I sent him to you to train in knighthood," Queen Morgawse cried, "and you made him a kitchen-knave! Shame on you, brother! And on you, too, Gawain!"

"Dear mother," said Sir Gawain. "I did not know he was my brother. Fifteen years ago, when I last saw him, he was a child at your knee."

"Neither did I know him," said King Arthur. "But God be thanked he has proved as noble a knight of his years as any now living."

"Shame on you, brother," cried Queen Morgawse again, "that you kept my son in the kitchen and fed him like a poor hog!"

"Fair sister," said King Arthur, patiently, "had you sent me word of his coming, this would not have happened."

"But I sent him to you well armed and horsed," she insisted, "and with gold and silver to spend."

"We knew nothing of this," said King Arthur, "till he departed. Now, sister, let the past pass, and let us be merry together. For he has proved a worshipful knight and that is my joy."

"But where is my young son now?" demanded Queen Morgawse.

"Sister," said King Arthur, "I will send at once in search of him; and if he is within these seven realms, he will quickly be found."

"Sire," said Sir Gawain, "with your leave I will set out now to find my brother."

"Lord King," said Sir Ironside, "there is no need to search the seven realms. For he told me that Dame Lyonesse, the lady of the Castle Perilous, whom I so shamefully besieged, was his lady. She will give you the best counsel as to where to find him."

"That is well said," said King Arthur. "I will send a messenger to her at once, and pray her to come to the Court with all the speed she can."

And, there and then, King Arthur had courteous letters written to Dame Lyonesse, and a messenger was at once sent forth with them. And day and night he rode till he reached the Castle Perilous.

XII. HOW A TOURNAMENT WAS HELD AT CASTLE PERILOUS

OW Dame Lyonesse was still with Fairhands and Linet at her brother's castle; so King Arthur's messenger was sent on to her there from the Castle Perilous. When she had read the letters he brought, she had letters written in reply, and bade the messenger ride back to King Arthur that she would follow in all haste.

Then she went to Fairhands and Sir Gringamore, and said: "Now advise me as to what I shall do and say at King Arthur's Court."

"My lady and my love," Fairhands replied, "I must now prepare myself to win you in fair fight. Offer to King Arthur to hold a tournament before your castle in two months' time, and that the knight who proves the best shall wed you and become lord of your lands."

"Let the tournament be between King Arthur's Knights of the Round Table on the one hand," suggested Sir Gringamore, "and the Knights of the Castle Perilous on the other. And let the tournament be open to all comers, and let all knights who come be free to choose whether to be of our party or the King's."

"And whoever asks, sweet lady," said Fairhands, "and however pressingly, do not reveal where I am. Say that wherever I may be now, it is certain I shall not fail to appear at the tournament."

All this Dame Lyonesse promised to do. After a tender leave-taking, she departed with an escort of her brother's knights, and so came without mishap to the Court at Caerleon-on-Usk. Here she was nobly received by King Arthur and Queen Guinevere and Queen Morgawse, who all found her beauty peerless.

They all questioned her closely as to where Fairhands was, and to all she prudently replied:

"Who can say? For such young knights do not stay long in one place when they are in search of adventures. But if the King will be so gracious as to grant me leave to do so, I will hold a tournament before my castle in two months' time, with my hand and my land as the prize. Wherever he may be now, I am sure that there you will hear news of Sir Gareth."

"That is well advised," said King Arthur. "For no knight can resist a tournament."

And indeed he and all his Knights of the Round Table began at once with delight to prepare for the tournament. And the tournament was made known throughout England, Wales and Scotland, Ireland, Cornwall and in all the Outer Isles, and in Brittany and in many other realms, so that those knights who tilted there would be matched with the most noble knights of the whole world.

Then Dame Lyonesse took her leave of King Arthur and Queen Guinevere and Queen Morgawse and all at the Court with great honour, and returned with her escort of knights to the Castle Perilous, where Fairhands and Linet and Sir Gringamore awaited her coming. And when she and Fairhands met, you may be sure that there were many kind looks and words between them.

And now great were the preparations at the Castle Perilous, to make provision for the lodging of so many knights and for food to feed them all, brought both by land and by water, by barge and by pack-horse train, so that nothing was lacking that could be got for gold and silver, or from field and forest, or from air or river or sea.

The first knights to arrive were Fairhands' vassals, Sir Ironside, the Green Knight, the Red Knight and the Blue Knight, each with his own company.

"Sir," they said to him, "we have taken upon ourselves to fight, with their agreement, against Sir Lancelot and the Knights of the Round Table. And this we have done for love of your lady, Dame Lyonesse, and of you, our Lord Gareth."

"That is well done," Fairhands praised them. "But do not speak my true name before any who come, and make no more of me than of the humblest knight who comes. For I do not wish it to be known who I am."

"Then I will lend you a ring," said Dame Lyonesse. "But I pray you to return it when the tournament is over, for to wear it increases my beauty. It can turn red to green, and blue to white, and so with all the colours; thus you will seem always in different armour, and so you will not be known."

"I thank you, mine own lady," said Fairhands, warmly.

So all was ready when King Arthur and his knights arrived two days before the tournament was to begin, and with them Queen Guinevere and Queen Morgawse and many other ladies. Dame Lyonesse welcomed them with every honour, and lodged them royally, and entertained them well with feasting and minstrelsy.

And now knights came riding in from many realms, both near and distant, so that the plain below the castle grew gay with a coloured town of tents.

On the third day all assembled; the heralds blew their trumpets, and the tournament began. Many a noble encounter took place; many a brave knight was unhorsed, many a strong spear broken, many a sharp sword drawn.

And in every course Fairhands rode, his armour changed its colour, so that it was now blue, now green, now red, now white, now yellow; and in every course he fought so well that from every side knights came riding about him, all calling:

"Knight of the Many Colours, well indeed have you jousted! I pray you, now make ready to joust with me!"

Soon that name, Knight of Many Colours, was on every knight's lips.

"Who is this Knight of Many Colours," all the Knights of the Round Table asked," who enforces himself to do such great deeds and never ceases?"

"This Knight of Many Colours," said King Arthur, "is the best of all the knights here."

And he asked many Knights of the Castle Perilous party who this Knight of Many Colours was; but not one of them could tell him.

XIII. HOW FAIRHANDS WON THE TOURNAMENT AND WAS WEDDED TO HIS LADY

OW at the end of the third day of the tournament, the victor was to be proclaimed. And towards the end of that day, Fairhands, feeling in need of a respite, rode aside and dismounted and sat on a mole-hill while he unlaced his helmet to cool his brow.

Then he knelt by the river, and took off his iron gauntlets, to leave his hands free to scoop up water to quench his thirst. And his dwarf, coming to him there, said to him:

"Master, let me take your ring, lest it fall into the river."

So Fairhands took off Dame Lyonesse's ring and handed it to his dwarf for safe-keeping. And when he had drunk, he put on his helm and his gauntlets again, and, forgetting the ring, mounted his steed and rode back to the tournament rested and refreshed.

The dwarf, watching him go, did not remind him of the ring, for he said to himself: "It is time my master was known!"

And as he watched him fighting, he saw that he fought like one having seven men's strength.

Now all at the tournament had noticed the height of the Knight of Many Colours; and now they saw this tall knight excelling his past exploits in armour of unchanging gold. So King Arthur sent for the heralds, and said to them:

"Go and ride near the tall knight in the golden armour and ask him his name, then proclaim him the victor of the tournament."

So the heralds rode as near to Fairhands as they could get, and the nearest of all saw written in letters of gold on Fairhands' helmet:

"This is Sir Gareth of Orkney."

So he cried with all his might:

"Here is Sir Gareth of Orkney, the victor of this tournament!"

And all the other heralds echoed him:

"Here is Sir Gareth of Orkney, the victor of this tournament!"

And all the Knights of the Round Table beheld him and waited, then pressed about him, crying:

"The Knight of Many Colours is proclaimed the victor!"

And all the knights of the Castle Perilous party cried:

"This is he who loves the lady of the castle, and she him!"

Then Fairhands' dwarf slipped away and ran to give her ring back to Dame Lyonesse.

"Where is my knight, dwarf?" she asked.

And he replied:

"Madam, he will not be long from you. And when he comes, he will bring you happy tidings."

Meanwhile, King Arthur embraced his nephew with great joy, and Sir Gawain threw away his shield and ran to his young brother and took him in his arms. And when Queen Morgawse saw her youngest son face to face, she tried to speak, but could not, but sank down in a swoon for gladness. And Fairhands comforted her so well that she soon recovered and was merry with the others.

Then King Arthur sent for Dame Lyonesse, and she came in haste, with her sister Linet and her brother Sir Gringamore. And the looks which passed between Fairhands and his lady were such that all men rejoiced to behold them.

"Fair Lady," said King Arthur to Dame Lyonesse, "here is the victor of your tournament. Will you have him for your husband?"

"Sire," she replied, "if I may not have him for my husband, I will have none. And if you give him his free choice, I dare say he will have me."

"Well, nephew," said King Arthur, "what say you to that?"

"Sire," said Fairhands, "that if I may not have her for my wife, I will go to the grave unwedded."

"Then," smiled King Arthur, "I must forward this marriage to the utmost of my power."

So it was settled that the wedding should be held at the Feast of Michaelmas, at Kynk Kenadon, the castle on the sands where Fairhands' adventures first began. And the tidings were carried there and then to all the other castles in the realm.

Then King Arthur gave a rich bracelet of gold to Dame Lyonesse, and Fairhands took a lover's leave of her till Michaelmas, and she rode back to her castle with Linet and Sir Gringamore, to start her own preparations for her wedding.

Meanwhile, there was saddling of queens' horses and of princes' horses and of knights' horses, and King Arthur and his fellowship rode away towards Kynk Kenadon, and Fairhands with them. And lord! the great joy Sir Lancelot made of Fairhands, and Fairhands of Sir Lancelot, for Fairhands loved Sir Lancelot beyond all other knights.

So it drew on to the Feast of Michaelmas, when Dame Lyonesse and Linet came to Kynk Kenadon in the safe-keeping of Sir Gringamore, their brother. And on Michaelmas Day Fairhands was married to Dame Lyonesse by the Bishop of Canterbury, and then Fairhands' vassals came to do homage to him.

The Green Knight came with his fifty knights, and begged that at the wedding feast he might be chamberlain and conduct the wedding guests to their seats. The Red Knight came with his three score knights, and begged that he might be butler and serve the wine. The Blue Knight came with his hundred knights, and begged that he might be sewer-chief and order the serving-men. And Sir Ironside came with his three hundred knights, and begged that he might be carver and carve the meats. And to each of them Fairhands replied:

"Since it pleases you to fill so humble an office, do so with my goodwill."

Then kings and queens, princes and earls, barons and knights sat down to the wedding feast; and after it there were revels and dancing, and music of harp and viol, and all manner of minstrelsy that was used in those days. And after the feast there was jousting for three days; but King Arthur forbade Fairhands to joust because he was newly-wed.

But wide lands and great riches King Arthur gave as a wedding gift to Fairhands and Dame Lyonesse, that they might live royally to their lives' end.

♦ THE END ♦

ABOUT THIS BOOK.

All the illustrations except one in this book are derived from medieval manuscripts. In English they are called "illuminations", because they lit up (illumined) the pages of the black-letter manuscripts with clear and brilliant colours, sometimes shining out of backgrounds of pure gold.

Both the black script and the glowing illustrations were done by hand. A wealthy book-lover would often have permanently in his household both a scribe and an artist, who did nothing but copy and illuminate manuscripts for his treasured book-collection.

When the universities were founded in the 12th. and 13th. centuries, the scholars who thronged to them needed books, and many of these scholars were poor. To meet this new need, workshops sprang up, clustered round the universities. The script and the illuminations were no longer so artistic, for they were the work of less skilled scribes and artists. But they were still all done by hand, for printing and picture-reproduction were not invented till the 15th. century.

Our one illustration which is not from an illumination is from a medieval woodcarving on a misericord in the choir of Lincoln Cathedral; you can see this on the end-papers. Misericords were narrow hinged seats built into the walls of the choir for the weary standing choristers to rest on in the days before there were choir-stalls. (That is why the misericord was given its name, which comes from the Latin and means "compassionate heart.") When you tip up these narrow seats, under them you find beautiful and often humorous medieval wood-carvings of scenes from the Bible, or from medieval legends, or even from daily life – such as boys stealing apples!

Our misericord, which was carved in 1380, shows Sir Owain's horse cut in half by the portcullis in our story of *The Lady of the Fountain*. For it was not only in the manuscript-illuminations that the stories of King Arthur and his knights were illustrated, but in every kind of medieval art and craftsmanship – corbels and capitals of stone pillars, statues, tapestries, murals, pavement tiles, embroideries, ceiling paintings, wooden caskets and trays, ivory caskets and combs, caskets and cases in leather, metal and enamel.

You will realise from this how large a space King Arthur and his knights occupied in the medieval mind, and what a wonderful heritage we have in stories such as those we have read.

TALES THE HARPER SANG

Medieval stories collected and retold by Isabel Wyatt
This is the third Waldorf Reader published by the Lanthorn press. The subject-matter is suitable for the sixth or seventh class along with or following the first study of medieval times.

Illustrations by	**Arne Klingborg and** Jean Francois de Barros
Lettering by	Stuart Page
Printed by	Alabaster Passmore & Sons Ltd
Published by	The Lanthorn Press Peredur East Grinstead Sussex